Homer's Iliad

Homer's
—
Iliad

RETOLD BY VÍTĚZSLAV KOCOUREK

TRANSLATED
BY VLADIMÍR VAŘECHA

ILLUSTRATIONS
BY JIŘÍ BĚHOUNEK

SUNBURST BOOKS

Homer's text retold by Vítězslav Kocourek
Translated by Vladimír Vařecha
Illustrations by Jiří Běhounek

Designed and produced by Aventinum
English language edition first published 1994 by
Sunburst Books, 65 Old Church Street,
London SW3 5BS

© 1993 Aventinum, Prague

ISBN 1-85778-030-2
Printed in the Slovak Republic
1/23/03/51-01

CONTENTS

PRELUDE

Many years ago, when the ancient Greeks believed that Mount Olympus was the home of the gods, who liked to interfere with the course of human lives, a huge navy assembled at the port of Aulis on the eastern coast of Greece. Altogether there were 1,186 ships rocking on the waves of the Aegean Sea and aboard them were 100,000 soldiers! For a whole year, soldiers from more than forty Greek kingdoms and states had been gathering at the port; swords had been sharpened, shields strengthened and spears ground. The army was led by Agamemnon, King of Mycenae and experienced commander, well known for his pride and his wealth. His warriors, who occupied more than one hundred ships, were joined by the troops of King

Diomedes, who ruled a region called Argos, while Nestor, the oldest of the kings, arrived with his two sons and many armed men from the town of Pylos in the south of Greece.

The warriors from the island of Crete were led by Idomeneus, who was distinguished by his brilliant use of the spear. King Aianthus of Salamis was famous for his courage in war. The numerous fighters from the islands of Zacynthus, Samos and Ithaca were under the command of Odysseus, the cleverest and most cunning of rulers. He had proved many times that if conflicts cannot be ended by fighting, it is possible to win by clever or cunning devices.

All the soldiers — both those who had won glory in the battles of the past and those about to fight for the first time — were united by a single aim. They were determined to destroy the proud, rich city of Troy, which was ruled by King Priam and which lay on the western coast of Asia Minor. They longed to break down the walls of Troy and to wreck the houses and palaces as a

punishment for the disgrace brought upon Menelaus, King of Sparta, which had also affected all Greeks. To make matters worse, the King had been insulted by an old friend and a welcome guest! The Greeks had to respond by going to war to punish those responsible.

The dreadful deed which had outraged all the Greek nobles had been carried out by Paris, Priam's son. He was the youngest of the King's sons and daughters and something strange had happened at his birth. Just before he was born, his mother, Queen Hecabe, had had an odd dream: she was bending over a crying newborn child, and when she took him in her arms, the baby turned into a flaming torch. The flames immediately spread, set fire to the palace and soon reduced the whole city to dust and ashes.

The distraught King called in twenty soothsayers or fortune-tellers to interpret the sense of the dream. They all agreed that it could mean only one thing: the son about to be born would cause a fire that would ruin Troy.

The King and Queen were so horrified that Priam finally decided that the baby should be put in a deserted place on the slope of Mount Ida where the most powerful god Zeus lived. They would rather have the baby starve to death or be eaten by a wild animal than let him cause suffering to an entire kingdom.

The family was convinced that the little boy would die in the wilderness. However, the wishes of the Olympian gods decided otherwise.

The baby was found by Agelaus, the King's shepherd, and as he had no children of his own, he took the boy home with him. He and his wife called him Paris.

Agelaus brought up Paris as if he were his own son. He taught him to look after the sheep, showed him how to carve wood and taught him how to play the pipe. Paris grew into a handsome young man, who knew how to cope with every emergency and who was not afraid of anything or anyone.

One day, Paris was resting under a huge oak tree, when suddenly he heard a rustling sound. Soon he recognized a fine, ringing voice: 'Don't be afraid, Paris, I am Hermes, messenger of the Olympian gods. I have come by order of Zeus, the ruler of gods and kings. He has chosen you to decide which of three goddesses is the most beautiful. The one you choose will receive from you a golden apple from the garden of the Hesperides. Now come and follow me.'

Standing in front of Paris was a young man with winged shoes on his feet and a golden twig in his hand. He was pointing towards a forest clearing where three women were standing on some grass. Each one was so beautiful that he could have handed the golden apple to all three of them.

One of the women, Hera, wife of the powerful Zeus, was the first to speak: 'If you choose me, Paris, I will shower you with wealth and you will rule over all the countries as far as the eye can see.'

Hardly had she spoken when the second goddess, Pallas Athene, the pampered daughter of Zeus, beckoned lightly with her hand and gave him a warm smile: 'If you acknowledge that I am the most beautiful, Paris, you shall become famous as the bravest hero of all.'

The third promise was made by Aphrodite, the young goddess of love and beauty: 'I offer you a gift far more precious than wealth and the glory of war. If you choose me, I will give you the most beautiful wife in the world, Helen, the Queen of Sparta, the daughter of Zeus.'

'Yes, goddess, you are the loveliest, and the golden apple rightly belongs to you!' Paris claimed and handed it to her. In that moment he won Aphrodite's favour forever — and the everlasting hatred of both Hera and Pallas Athene.

Before another year had passed, King Priam organized a

games contest. He hoped this would help to cheer up his wife Hecube who was still tortured by guilt for having allowed her baby to be abandoned in the wilderness. To give the games some glamour, the King called all the leading nobles to take part in the contest. Even the King's sons were to join in. The winner's prize was to be a young bull of a rare breed, the best from a herd looked after by Paris. Paris was extremely fond of the animal and found it hard to part with the young bull. So he decided to try and win him back in the contest.

It was a great surprise to everyone when he won three successive bouts of fighting and even overcame his brothers, although, of course, he did not know they were his brothers, including Hector, who was the strongest. However, there was even greater excitement when, just before the King was to announce the unexpected winner, Cassandra, the King's daughter, suddenly appeared in the banqueting hall. Cassandra had the power to tell the future.

'Your Majesty, you ought to offer a drink to the gods to thank them for sending back your lost son,' she said in an excited voice. 'Rejoice, King, and be happy, Queen. But beware. The gods never take back their prophecies and the dream which the Queen had will still come true. Father, crown Paris with the laurel crown of victory, give him many gifts, but do not let him stay in our palace for any length of time!'

Their joy over the unexpected reunion with their son was stronger then Cassandra's words of warning. As though eager to make up to their son for the years he had lost with them, the King and Queen both hugged Paris and ordered that he should be dressed in magnificent clothes, have rooms fit for a royal prince prepared for him, and that maids should be chosen to take good care of their new-found son.

From then on, Paris lived with his royal parents, brothers and sisters, and as the weeks and months passed, he soon forgot that he had once been a shepherd and had met the goddess Aphrodite. He could

hardly believe his eyes when she appeared at his bedside one evening.

'Dear Paris, I have not forgotten what I promised you,' she said in her gentle, musical voice, as she held the golden apple from the garden of the Hesperides. 'The time has come for you to get ready to set out for Sparta in the country of Laconia. There, in the court of King Menelaus, you will find Helen, the most beautiful woman on earth. You are sure to win her heart. Don't be afraid, for I will shield and protect you!'

She nodded gracefully and disappeared like a morning mist on the surface of a lake.

Obedient to what the goddess had said, Paris set out on his journey. Laconia was a wild land, full of unclimbable rocks,

dangerous gorges and precipices, but King Menelaus's palace was famous for its comfort and splendour. The spacious halls were decorated in gold, the seats had backs of ivory, food was served on silver dishes, and there were many wonderful drinking glasses and jugs.

However, Paris was far more enchanted by the beauty of Queen Helen. He was bewitched by her when she sat next to him at the banquet given by King Menelaus in honour of Paris, the Trojan Prince. Her beauty made him feel faint. He soon found himself deeply in love and Helen also felt the same for him. Helen thought of Paris all the time and just seeing him made her breathless. They both felt as if they were burning up with love for each other, but they did not admit it at first. Before long, however, their feelings were so strong that they were swept off their feet.

Shortly after Paris's arrival in Sparta, an unexpected duty called King Menelaus away from his palace for a few days on a visit to the island of Crete.

Menelaus asked his wife to take care of their visitor while he was away. He did not suspect that they were deeply in love with each other, and only wanted to be together for evermore. As soon as Menelaus had left the city, Paris told Helen what they should do:

'Helen, you are the most beautiful woman I have ever seen. We can no longer stay here — for the goddess Aphrodite has prepared the path for our love. My ship is waiting in the port. Collect what you need and let us escape. We will sail together to Troy! No other woman is as beautiful as you!'

Helen hardly hesitated for she knew what she truly wanted to do. She gathered together her jewels, put on the dress which she was wearing when she first

saw Paris, kissed her daughter, Hermion, said goodbye and left. She did not even turn back to have one last look at the palace.

Three days later, Helen and Paris passed through the main city gate of Troy. Both were given a warm welcome, and no one took any notice of Cassandra who was crying in a quiet corner. Nor did anyone know that, back in Sparta, King Menelaus was standing on the steps of his palace where the words of his chief servant had hit him like a thunderbolt: 'Oh, King! Your wife has been stolen; your guest kidnapped her and took her to Troy with him!' As Helen was being welcomed by the Trojans, Menelaus declared: 'Have my horses and chariot made ready. I will go to Mycenae to see my brother, Agamemnon. This wrongdoing must be put right. Troy must be punished.'

One of the noblemen who was to take part in the expedition against Troy was the famous hero, Achilles, son of Peleus, King of the Myrmidons, and of the beautiful and kind sea nymph Thetis. Peleus once caught sight of Thetis in a bay where a dolphin used to carry her on his back. For a long time after this Peleus used to hide in the undergrowth, waiting for a chance to tell Thetis how much he loved her. However, it was by no means easy to approach Thetis. Peleus might never have won Thetis's heart if Proteus, the old man of the sea, had not told him how to get the better of her. One day, when Thetis once again came riding on the dolphin, Peleus, acting on Proteus's advice, went into the cave after her and tied her firmly with ropes. Thetis turned herself into a bird, a tiger, and a snake, but Peleus did not loosen the knots until she had promised to marry him. He, in turn, had to promise that he would never be cross with her. If he broke his promise, Thetis would leave him and become free again.

The wedding took place in the cave of a wise centaur, a creature half man and half horse. The centaur was called Cheiron, and the wedding was attended by many of the King's friends as well as many gods who showered

a wealth of gifts and favours on the newly-weds. Poseidon, ruler of the seas, gave Peleus two immortal horses, Balius and Xanthus, Cheiron the centaur gave them an unbreakable ash spear, and Zeus, ruler of Olympus, presented Peleus with some magnificent, sparkling armour made by Hephaistos, the blacksmith of the Olympian gods.

During the wedding celebration, three old women with wrinkled faces and dressed in dazzling white robes suddenly appeared. They were the Fates who hold the spindle of the future and spin the threads of future events. The first old woman spoke the following words: 'Before long, you will have a son and you will call him Achilles. People will admire him, because he will be better than everyone else, both in his looks and in his courage.'

'No one shall be faster at running, no one shall beat him in wrestling, and no one shall defeat him on the battlefield,' said the second.

Then the third of the old women was heard saying, 'He will decide the fall of the city of Troy. And only a Trojan arrow can kill him.'

'Here is to the glory of the hero who will never be outdone!' exclaimed Peleus, overjoyed, when the words of the prophecy had faded and the Fates had disappeared. Then he called on wedding guests to drink a toast. However, he had not noticed that Thetis had a very worried look on her face.

Thetis adored her son from the moment he was born. First, she rubbed him with the sweet-smelling ointment of ambrosia which guarantees everlasting youth. Then she set out for the river Styx in the underworld where she submerged the boy in its waters. This bathing made it impossible for anyone to wound him anywhere on his body apart from a small part of his heels where Thetis held him. Finally, she wanted to entrust his body to the flames of a midnight fire which would consume his human form.

As Thetis was laying the child upon the flames of the fire, Peleus woke up. Horrified by what he saw, he leaped to his wife, pulled his son from her arms, and shouted angrily at her. Thetis's eyes filled with tears. She looked lovingly at her son and her husband and said, 'Oh, King Peleus, why ever did you break your promise? Have you forgotten the wording of our agreement? Goodbye, dear husband. Your show of anger has resulted in the two of us never seeing each other again!'

So saying, she disappeared like a light breeze and flowed into the sea. Peleus was left alone, with a baby son to care for.

When Achilles was six years old, his father asked the wise centaur Cheiron to look after him. The boy soon learned to recognize medicinal plants and to use them to prepare ointments for healing wounds and illnesses. He also learned to play the lute,

to dance and sing, as well as how to hunt. He was unafraid as he hunted both quick-footed stags and thick-set boars; he could heal wounds better than Cheiron could and when he recited verses or played the lute, he always pleased his audience. Cheiron was glad that Achilles learned so well and he did not look forward to his leaving. Thetis was also worried about it. Before long, he would grow out of boyish pastimes and Thetis would see her son wearing armour and racing with a sword or spear on a war chariot.

Thetis was right to worry when she heard that, under the leadership of King Agamemnon, an army was being raised against Troy. Since Achilles had returned to his native land of the Myrmidons, he had proved time and time again that he was a fearless warrior and had earned the reputation of an undaunted hero. However, the more his mother was troubled, the more she kept reminding herself of the words of Calchas, the priest who foretold the future: 'The Greeks shall not conquer Troy unless

Achilles helps them to win.' Thetis was terrified and she had only one thought: to prevent Achilles from joining that army, to hide him somewhere to ensure his safety.

Eventually, she hit upon the idea that she could disguise Achilles as a girl and take him to the palace of King Lycomedes on the island of Scyros. No one would look for him there, and he would be safely hidden among the King's daughters.

At night, when Achilles was deeply asleep, Thetis called two of her dolphins and settled her son on their backs. She asked the god Poseidon to calm the surface of the waters and ventured out upon the sea. In the morning they stood in front of the palace of King Lycomedes. His beautiful daughters were just walking out of the gates. Achilles did not object when his mother dressed him as a girl and led him to the royal hall.

'King Lycomedes,' she said, when they faced the ruler of the island, 'this is Achilles's sister. Please educate her as you would your own daughters. Up until

now, she has enjoyed boys' hobbies and pursuits more than girls'. Shooting with a bow and arrow are more fascinating to her than weaving wool, and the spear means more to her than sparkling earrings. I should be happy if she kept away from men's hobbies.'

The King looked at Achilles with pleasure and he nodded with a kind smile: 'As you wish.' Thetis was very relieved; it was a weight off her mind. Now she believed that her son would be saved from taking part in the war with Troy. 'Let the Greeks fight King Priam and his allies. But the blood that will be shed outside Troy will not be that of Achilles.'

However, all the time while Achilles in disguise was enjoying the company of the King's daughters, there was unrest in the Greek camp at Aulis. Everybody had expected that Achilles would be the first to join their ranks. The mere mention of his name struck terror into their enemies' hearts, so they were very confused when he was nowhere to be found. Agamemnon sent messengers

and spies into all corners of the land but one after another came back empty-handed. It was as if Achilles had vanished into thin air. Agamemnon was forced to ask the soothsayer Calchas whether he could give some advice about where the famous hero could be found.

'I can see a sea, an island and a magnificent palace as well as a party of young girls who are dancing, singing and making daisy chains. The King of the island of Scyros is smiling. Achilles is not there, and yet he is there,' was the response.

A group of nobles decided to send Odysseus, known for his cleverness, Diomedes, the ruler of Argos, and the experienced soldier, Agyrtes, to the island. At Odysseus's suggestion they filled the ship with a cargo of bracelets, coronets, earrings and girls' dresses, plus a war-shield and a spear. Disguised as merchants, they landed on the shores of the island of Scyros.

King Lycomedes welcomed them to his palace and gave them the best rooms to rest in. Later he called his twelve

daughters to appear before him to dance to the accompaniment of lutes and pipes to entertain the guests. When they had finished, Odysseus turned to the King, saying, 'Ruler of the island, never in my life have I seen a more splendid dance. Your daughters could easily perform before Zeus himself. You must let us reward them with some gifts. Let them choose what they would like from the merchandise that we have brought with us.'

Lycomedes was flattered by Odysseus's words. He nodded and Diomedes spread out the shining bracelets, glittering earrings and a variety of brooches, hairpins and gold-embroidered veils. Mixed with all these was the sword and shield. The daughters were spoiled for choice. They tried on coronets, wound scarves round their necks, and clipped on the earrings. Suddenly a trumpet, the clatter of weapons and a battlecry could be heard — it was Argytes who, together with Odysseus, had deliberately caused uproar in the courtyard. The girls shrieked in terror and ran away. However, one of them lunged forward, put a shield on her arm, gripped the sword, and brandished it over her head.

At that moment Odysseus leaped forward and undid the girl's dress, exclaiming, 'You are none other than Achilles! But why are you hiding disguised as a girl? You have already proved how good you are in battles. Would you prefer to spin or operate a weaver's loom while the Greeks are fighting the Trojans? Would you like the terrible disgrace of Menelaus to go unpunished? Tell Lycomedes who you really are, and join us. The Greeks are eagerly waiting for you in Aulis!'

Achilles was deeply shaken by these words. How could he stay out of danger when he was needed in battle? He bent his head and, throwing off his disguise, bowed to the King:

'Forgive me, kind ruler, for deceiving you. But you must understand how worried my mother is. My mother, Thetis, wanted to protect me from the danger threatening me in Troy. But I am strong and can cope with whatever the future may hold in store for me! After all, every man who has done his duty will be rewarded, even those who lose their lives when they are young. But tell me — what use is a long life if you have not done everything worthwhile?'

It was hard for Achilles to say goodbye to King Lycomedes and even harder to part from his ageing father when he returned to his native Thessaly. Peleus could not bear to think of his son going to war with Troy. So he requested that a sacrificial stake be set on fire to satisfy the gods. He gave Achilles the magnificent armour he had received as a wedding present from Zeus. He also gave him Cheiron's extremely heavy and unbreakable ash spear and two of Poseidon's immortal horses, Balius and Xanthus. Peleus then said goodbye to his son, who set off for Aulis with forty ships.

As his ship was approaching the port, a huge wave carrying Thetis rose up in front of the vessel. She was being carried by dolphins towards the coast of Asia Minor, into the sea waters near

Troy so that she could be as close as possible to her son and help him in the forthcoming battle. When she saw Achilles standing proudly on the prow of his ship, her heart was full of sorrow. She felt that she was the unhappiest mother on earth.

At that time, whenever an army was preparing to go into battle or to strike at the enemy, it was usual to please the Olympian gods with a burnt offering of a ram, a bull or a boar, or at least to learn from them what lay ahead. Before battle, the Greek leaders gathered under a plane tree grove, while the priests set fire to a stake near the altar. They all began to worship the gods and prayed to be given a good wind for sailing.

The smoke from the fire rose and rose and covered the altar when, all of a sudden, a hideous snake with a blood-red back shot up from under the altar. He hissed, rose and wound up his way up to the top of a plane tree where eight young sparrows were huddled in the leaves on the top branch. The snake stared at them, rushed at them and strangled one after the other. He then attacked the mother sparrow who was piping desperately and trying in vain to protect her young. The hideous serpent then slid down the tree and, having stiffened at the foot of the altar, turned to stone.

Everyone was paralysed and filled with horror at the strange event. Some thought that Zeus was sending a warning; others believed that he was feeling offended by one of the lesser Olympians and expected them to appease him. When they asked the soothsayer, Calchas, to explain the mysterious phenomenon, this was his reply: 'The nine strangled birds signify nine years. This is how long you are destined to fight the Trojans. Only in the tenth year will the walls tumble down and the city be destroyed.'

The prospect of so many years of fighting made the Greek nobles despondent. However, Agamemnon was the first to pull himself together, and he began to rouse his comrades: 'Why are you standing here like a flock of sheep? We can't change what

the gods have forecast. If we are to fight nine years, let us begin our struggle as soon as possible. Let us set sail now, for the most favourable winds are blowing!'

'You have said what we all feel,' exclaimed Menelaus, and Achilles, Odysseus, Nestor, Diomedes and the other noblemen agreed. Once again the Greek warriors were determined to fight the Trojans, and as the new day dawned the fleet was ready to sail.

However, the wind had turned to the wrong direction and the sea was too rough to allow the ships a safe passage. Several days later, the wind died down and was replaced by a dead calm so that not even a leaf stirred. The white sails of the ships were floppy and drooping. Once again, Agamemnon decided to seek Calchas's advice, but what he heard was nearly enough to drive him mad:

'Agamemnon, you have greatly offended Artemis, the goddess of the hunt, when you killed her deer in her sacred grove! What's more, you boasted of being a better marksman than Artemis herself. Unless you sacrifice your daughter Iphigenia on this altar where the red snake turned to stone, the Greek ships are doomed never to set sail from Aulis!'

Agamemnon had only one night to decide what to do. After consulting his nobles, he called for Iphigenia to come to Aulis immediately. She and her mother, Clytemnestra, were to be told that an engagement feast with the famous hero Achilles was being prepared.

In his commander's tent where the leading noblemen including Menelaus, Nestor, Achilles, Ajax and Odysseus were assembled, Agamemnon revealed to his wife and daughter the truth about the abominable sacrifice demanded by the goddess Artemis. Queen Clytemnestra turned deadly pale, and gasping for breath, she plunged towards the King of the Myrmidons:

'Achilles, you should have been engaged to Iphigenia, so save my daughter now, don't let her end her life when she is so young.' Clytemnestra cried so despairingly that the hero's heart melted and he touched the hilt of his sword. But who was he to draw it against? He could not use it to undo the will of the goddess. Should he use it against Ajax, Menelaus or Odysseus who had no sympathy with Iphigenia's fate? They had not even seen Troy, so how could he soak the ground with Greek blood? They all stared at each other. Then Achilles felt Iphigenia's hand softly touch his shoulder.

'Keep your sword in the scabbard, Achilles,' she said gently. 'I do not want so much as a single drop of Greek blood to be shed in vain! If there is no other way of satisfying the goddess Artemis, I am ready to be sacrificed. The ships will set sail and when Troy is finally destroyed all men will gratefully remember my sacrifice and will honour me for ever.'

Moved by what she had said,

Agamemnon hugged his daughter, then her weeping mother clasped Iphigenia in her arms, and her brother Orestes did the same. With a group of noblemen, they accompanied her to the altar where Calchas was waiting for her. He put the sacrificial knife into a golden basket, put a crown of fresh flowers on Iphigenia's head and raised both his arms and looked upwards into the tops of the plane trees. Then he let his arms drop slowly and seized the sacrificial knife. The glittering knife flashed through the air. Suddenly, there was the noise of thunder and the altar was enveloped in a thick black cloud. When the cloud had disappeared, there was a snow-white deer where Iphigenia had been standing.

'Let us thank the goddess Artemis,' cried Calchas. 'She was

testing your devotion, Agamemnon, but she certainly didn't want your daughter to die. Instead she made her a priestess in her temple in Tauris, and laid this dazzling white deer on the altar. Your sacrifice has been accepted, the road to Troy is free!'

As if to confirm these words, a light breeze developed, and became stronger and stronger, swelling the white sails of the ships. The leaders and the ordinary soldiers were gathering round the ships shouting enthusiastically again and again, 'Let us thank the goddess for the wind. Now we shall soon be at the gates of Troy, and shall soon punish her rulers!'

The fleet set sail a few days later and landed at night in a bay beneath a rocky headland. The Greeks couldn't wait to meet their enemy, and as they got off the ships they defeated their opponents who put up a stiff resistance. Only at dawn did they come to realize their fatal mistake. They hadn't landed on the coast of Troy, but on the shore of the island of Mysia. To make matters worse,

Telephus, King of the Mysians, had suffered a deep wound in a fight with Achilles. Telephus had always been a friend of the Greeks and he had such an excellent knowledge of the neighbouring seas that Agamemnon wanted him to be a true ally. Fortunately, Odysseus remembered an ancient prophecy of the Delphic oracle that the wound sustained by Telephus in a fight could only be healed by the one who had inflicted it. So, on Odysseus's advice, Achilles scraped some iron off the point of his spear and poured it on the injured place. Sure enough, the wound healed shortly afterwards.

Having recovered, Telephus piloted the Greek fleet across the sea and the whole expedition made another stop on the deserted island of Chrysos to make a sacrifice to the gods. The warriors found it very hard to make their way through the thickets and the undergrowth and it took them more than half a day to find the sacrificial altar which had been built by the hero Jason during his search for the

Golden Fleece. Just as they had found it, Philoctetes, King of Thessaly, reached for his sword to cut a way through the tangled woods. The next moment, he howled with pain and grabbed his foot which had been bitten by an enormous snake. The foot swelled and the wound caused by the snake's fangs began to spread a foul smell.

The unfortunate man, who was wailing loudly, was carried to the ship and taken to Podaleirius, the surgeon. First, he sprinkled the injured place with some healing powder; the next day he poured some liquid over it, but it was no use. Philoctetes cried day and night, the wound festered and the smell became so intolerable that everybody fled from the unfortunate hero. It was clear that he could not take part in the expedition in the state he was in, but nobody dared say so.

It was only after sailing near to the island of Lemnos that Odysseus plucked up the courage.

'Let us leave Philoctetes on the island. It has many deer and fresh water, and he will be able to recover his strength here,' he said. 'His snake bite will heal and after a time, when he is strong enough, he can rejoin the expedition.'

All agreed with Odysseus's suggestion. The sleeping Philoctetes was carried to the shore and the fleet set sail for Troy.

Before long, 1,186 ships darkened the entire horizon along the coast of Troy. The Trojans would certainly have been terrified at the mere sight of such a military force if it had not been for one of King Priam's sons, Helenus, a priest who foretold the future. He encouraged the Trojans with his prophetic claim that the gods would not tolerate the fall of a city whose founder was a friend of Zeus. Yet another event raised the Trojans' spirits, when another ancient prophecy

was fulfilled. This claimed that the first of the Greeks to touch Trojan soil with his feet would do so in peril of his life. Odysseus avoided the prophecy — he first threw his shield on to the mainland and then jumped upon it. Although he was standing on Trojan soil, he did not really touch it! But the young warrior Protesilaus, who followed him eagerly, landed directly on the mainland. He was immediately killed by a spear flung by Hector, the dearest son of King Priam and the bravest of the Trojan heroes.

As if in retaliation for the death of Protesilaus, Achilles himself leaped on to the mainland, so forcefully that a spring burst from the ground on the spot where he landed. The Trojans rushed forward, lead by King Kyknos, who was protected by an armour of nine layers of ox hides. Dozens of men clashed together and all that could be heard was the ringing of the swords and the roar of the enraged Kyknos. Kyknos's cry soon became a croak, and, through the falling clouds of dust, Achilles was seen kneeling over Kyknos. Achilles was strangling him with a couple of straps from Kyknos's own helmet and no matter how violently the big man tossed about, Achilles held on. Kyknos died soon and he lay like the trunk of a fallen tree. Seeing this, the Trojans quickly withdrew behind the city walls.

The day after the first encounter, the Greeks set about building a camp. They pulled the ships on to dry land, arranged them into a semicircle with their prows facing the sea, and between them set up tents made of hides. Then they dug a protective moat between Troy and the camp and built a mound with wooden piles and turrets. When the camp was set up, the leaders held a council of war.

'Wouldn't it be advisable to try and settle everything peacefully?' suggested Odysseus, who had

left behind his wife Penelope with his little son Telemachus and who had reluctantly joined the expedition. 'We have already captured Polydor, Priam's youngest son. We could offer him to the Trojans in exchange for Helen and thereby save the lives of Greek men. Indeed, to exchange a prince of royal blood for a prince's wife is no disgrace for either side. I am ready to try to negotiate a settlement. Choose who should come with me.'

The leaders accepted Odysseus's proposal and decided that Menelaus would accompany Odysseus. King Priam warmly received the two men and he listened carefully to Odysseus's proposal. Priam's counsellor, Antenor, supported the proposal and declared that if the Trojans rejected such an idea, they would be waging an unjust war and the gods would probably punish them for it. However, the sensible words of Antenor were rebuked by Priam's sons, particularly Paris and Antimachus.

'Antenor, you are either a fool or a traitor!' Paris shouted. 'Have you counted the multitude of ships and tents in front of our walls? They have come armed to the teeth and you believe that if we give Helen back to them, they will simply pull out and go home without shooting a single arrow? After all, why should we return Helen to them when she came to us as my wife and because she wanted to? She worships our gods and respects our customs, so she is ours, even if she was once Menelaus's wife!'

Antimachus even exclaimed, 'If you want to negotiate, in exchange for Polydor, we will give you our sister Cassandra and may add Polyxene into the bargain. They are young and pretty and are sure to get a good dowry!'

'We have not come here to do such bargaining,' said Menelaus, unable to contain himself over such an offensive speech. Priam's sons reached for their swords and they would have killed Menelaus and Odysseus if Priam and Antenor had not stopped them.

The talking had come to nothing and the peaceful attempt to resolve the dispute caused by

the abduction of the beautiful Queen of Sparta had ended in failure.

A period of merciless fighting followed. The walls and the plains in front of the city and also near the Greek camp saw the two sides clashing repeatedly. The Greeks made many attempts to storm the walls of Troy, but the city put up valiant resistance, and it was aided by its numerous allies. Of course, the Greeks destroyed many neighbouring lands. Achilles alone plundered the isle of Tenedos, routed Pedasos and sacked the city of Lymessos, bringing with him, among other things, two captives. These were Chryseïs, daughter of Apollo's priest Chryses, and Briseïs, daughter of the priest Brises, both very beautiful young girls.

Nevertheless, neither the siege nor the devastation achieved their goal. Troy went on resisting. Cruelty was repaid with even greater cruelty. Hatred was growing and tiredness set in, for time was passing and the prophecy was being fulfilled.

In the tenth year of fighting, something happened that was to change the whole destiny of the war.

And Homer, an unknown blind singer of ancient times, turned into a poem the events of the last fifty-one days of the Trojan war. The epic describes the honour and heroism, courage and fear, and the greatness and cruelty of war. The name he gave to this great story is *The Iliad.*

The two captives and the quarrel between the commanders

THE TWO CAPTIVES AND THE QUARREL
BETWEEN THE COMMANDERS

The Greek camp was buzzing with panic such as no one had experienced since the armies had last come to Troy. For ten years, the Greeks had been fighting a life-and-death struggle, showing their strength in the pitiless bloody killing, but not even the appalling cruelty of those battles had been so terrifying as the events of the previous nine days. Men on sentry duty would suddenly drop down as if they had been hit by a poisoned arrow, others would unexpectedly drop dead in their tents, while some were struck down as they were strolling on the seashore. The bodies of the dead turned black and gave off a revolting

stench just like the rotting flesh of animals, such as mules, goats, sheep and even dogs, which were afflicted with the same deadly illness.

There was no doubt that the illness was widespread and that it was a vengeance of the gods for a broken promise or an insult. On the tenth day, Achilles suggested that all the leaders should get together to decide what to do next. Every man had to put forward his own proposal, but most importantly they were to ask Calchas the cause of these terrible events and how they could be stopped. Otherwise they would have no alternative but to launch the ships, sail back and wait until things improved.

The Assembly accepted Achilles's proposition — they had no choice when men were panicking, not knowing whether they would be alive or dead within the hour. One question occupied them all. When was this horror going to end? Why were the Greeks being so afflicted and what were they being punished for?

'Is it you of all men, son of Peleus, who is asking this?' said Calchas, the prophet, when Achilles put the question to him on behalf of the leaders. 'I will tell you, but first promise me that no one will lay his hands on me for what I am going to say! I am afraid that what I have to say will make someone fly into a rage against me…'

'Go on, speak and don't be afraid, Calchas!' Achilles replied. 'For you will only be interpreting the words of the prophecy and not making judgements of your own. And I give you my word that I will always stand by you and protect you from anyone who might want to attack you, even if it should be our leader Agamemnon himself!'

'Now you have spoken the name,' said Calchas. 'It is Agamemnon who is the cause of all our present troubles. The plague has been sent by Apollo, son of Zeus, for offending his priest, Chryses. You must remember how he and his servants came here only a few days ago. They struggled under the weight of caskets which contained precious gifts. With

THE TWO CAPTIVES AND THE QUARREL
BETWEEN THE COMMANDERS

these the unhappy father wanted to ransom his daughter whom you, Achilles, had captured and given to Agamemnon as his slave. But Agamemnon roughly rejected her father's claim and laughing chased him away. Finally he threatened the feeble old man with disgrace and death if he dared to repeat his claim ever again. That made Apollo very angry and he sent this terrible illness to us. The plague will not disappear until Chryses's daughter is returned to her father, without any ransoms, without conditions, and with a sacred offering to satisfy Apollo.'

'Calchas, you prophet of evil,' Agamemnon burst out when the priest finished his speech, 'you have never prophesied anything to my advantage in all my life! Already once before, in Aulis, I had to offer a sacrifice to the goddess Artemis to ensure the success of the expedition. If it is me, as you declare, who is the cause of the plague, I am willing to give his daughter back to Chryses. Of course, she is my best slave — skilful with her hands, well-spoken and very

pretty, too. And it is only right that I should be given a replacement for her!'

'Don't be so mean, Agamemnon!' cried Achilles. 'What harm will it do you to give up one slave? When we take Troy, you shall have ten times as many. But surely you are not going to take away another man's prize?'

'How two-faced of you, Achilles, to speak like that,' fumed the Greeks' leader. 'You don't want to lose anything, but you are ready to give away what belongs to others. No, no — I must have some compensation. And I will choose it according to my own taste.'

'How selfish of you, Agamemnon,' exclaimed Achilles, his voice breaking with anger. 'As if I have never shared my rewards with anyone. You would always have more than my warriors. The truth is that the Myrmidons marched into battle first to help Menelaus. The Trojans had never done any harm to us, never robbed us of so much as a single cow. It was on your brother's account that

we went to battle to see his honour restored. And now I have to listen to your ranting. Listen to me, Agamemnon. We will return home — we shall be better off there — and you can go on fighting here if you want.'

'Do you expect me to beg you to stay?' said Agamemnon, outraged. 'There are others who respect me and will stay here with me. Go back home and take your Myrmidons with you! Anyway you are always causing trouble and quarrels. But what I have said holds good: as I must give up Chryses's daughter, you shall give me the daughter of

Brises in compensation. And if you do not bring her to me, I will come and fetch her, even if I have to take her by force, take it from me. Don't forget I am still the supreme commander here!'

'That's what you are!' rejoined the King of the Myrmidons, and he reached for his sword. At that moment, the goddess Pallas Athene herself appeared at his side. 'Do not be ruled by your feelings, Achilles!' she told him. 'Your time will come. One day they will all be begging you to forget the insult which has made your blood boil. You will be granted satisfaction greater than any gifts. Trust me.'

'Of course, noble goddess,' was all that Achilles managed to say, for the next moment the image of the goddess dissolved. He let go off his sword and thundered at Agamemnon, 'You are the supreme commander, but you are as cowardly as a hare and as rude as a dog. One day you will regret that you offended the bravest of all Greek heroes!'

The two commanders stared hard at each other until Nestor, the old King of Pylos, broke the silence. 'Agamemnon! Achilles! Can't you be more tolerant with each other?' he began to chide them. 'If Priam or one of his sons were here, he would rejoice seeing the Greek leaders arguing instead of racking their brains on how to assault the walls of Troy. I am older than both of you and have known many brave heroes in different wars, but none of them behaved like this. Take my good advice. You, Achilles, acknowledge Agamemnon as your supreme commander, and you, Agamemnon, try not to deprive him of his war prizes!'

'So that he can pick another quarrel in future?' retorted Agamemnon. 'Indeed, all he would like to do is to give orders and tell everyone else what to do. I acknowledge Achilles's military strength, that is surely a gift of the gods. But does this give him a right to call me such dreadful names before the whole council of war?'

'I would have to be a coward and not a soldier if I were to agree with your every word. I am not going to fight you for Briseïs, although she is equally as dear

to me as the daughter of Chryses is to you. Now I am going back to my ships and we shall see how you will get on without me. I am not going to fight the Trojans with you any more.' With those words Achilles turned on his heel and stalked away from the commanders.

Everybody was silent; no one spoke in favour of Thetis's son, some out of respect for Agamemnon, others hoping that Achilles would change his mind later on. Was it possible, they wondered, to fall out with a longstanding war companion because of one captured girl, no matter how beautiful and kind she was? Although many hoped that Achilles would eventually change his mind, they hoped in vain.

A fast ship with twenty oarsmen, commanded by Odysseus, was already taking away Chryses's daughter when Agamemnon's two messengers, Talthybius and Eurybates, entered Achilles's tent. They did not find him there, but nearby on the seashore, gloomy and looking into the distance. They hardly dared to speak to him, but he spoke first and, strangely enough, in a kind manner.

'How do you do, messengers? I was expecting you,' he said calmly and without anger. 'I know why you have come and I also know that you are not to blame for anything. Why should I dislike you when Agamemnon was to blame for everything? Now go back to my tent; my friend Patroclus will hand over to you the lovely Briseïs – and the two of you will be my witness before the immortal gods and mortal men that I swear to repay Agamemnon's ruthlessness in the same way. One day, when he is in trouble, when he comes to beg me for help, I will be just as stubborn as he is now!'

Both Agamemnon's messengers heard the hero's words in silence and it was also in silence that Patroclus handed over the captured Briseïs. As they were taking her away, they saw clouds of bluish smoke rising from where the altars had been set up in the camp.

'The sacrifice of calves and bullocks to appease angry Apollo has begun. At last the sickness

with which he has punished us will disappear,' said Talthybius with relief in his voice. They stopped walking as Eurybates pointed towards the shore where Achilles was sitting with his head buried in his hands.

'Look, Achilles is sad and sorry. I would even say that he is crying,' muttered Eurybates.

Talthybius nodded and, some moments later, he shook his head and added in a whisper, 'And so is the girl we are taking to Agamemnon, I believe ...'

Achilles was hardly aware of how long he had been sitting on the seashore, extremely downcast and saddened by the loss of the girl he had fallen in love with. Then Thetis, his divine mother, emerged from the waves in front of him. She had heard her son's quiet sobbing in her palace under the sea, and at once came up to see him.

'Achilles, my darling son, tell me what is troubling you. I feel sure I will be able to help you in this sadness which is tearing you apart,' she said soothingly, as she sat down at his side and gently stroked his arm.

'Oh, my divine mother, I, your famous son, have been greatly insulted. Agamemnon has deprived me of a girl who was mine by right and declared in front of all the leaders the accusation that in battle I gather prizes for my own benefit. You told me many times that I had to expect a life which, although it would not be long, was to be full of glory and respect. Now I have been offended as if I had never meant anything at all. Oh mother, you have always said that the mighty Zeus is a friend of yours. Please go and beg him to intervene − perhaps only for your sake − to make all the Greeks realize what crime Agamemnon committed when he offended his most powerful fighter. Let Zeus allow the Trojans to be victorious and let the Greeks find out what it is like to fight without Achilles!'

'My dearest son, I am very sorry to hear that it was you whom he had degraded so terribly,' moaned Thetis, her heart nearly bursting with sorrow. 'You have done well to give up your ships. Stay here, don't go back to

the fighting. I will find Zeus and speak to him as soon as he returns from his journey to the Aethiopians. Until then, do not lose heart, Achilles. I will help you as much as I can.'

Then the beautiful sea goddess once again took her son in her arms, kissed him gently on his forehead and drifted back into the sea, her real home.

A FAMILY QUARREL ON MOUNT OLYMPUS

It was twelve days before the day finally arrived when Zeus, accompanied by other gods and goddesses, returned to his magnificent palace, built from gold and precious stones on Mount Olympus. Hardly had he sat down on his throne when Thetis rose from the sea like a feather towards Zeus's seat above the clouds.

Kneeling in front of him she said, 'Father Zeus, ruler of gods and men, please listen to what

I have to say. I don't need help, noble King, but my son does. He has been insulted by Agamemnon and has had to leave the people he was staying with. As you are so powerful, punish Agamemnon by letting the Trojans win some battles. Let the Greeks realize that they are never going to defeat the Trojans without Achilles, and let them beg Achilles to help them!'

Zeus found himself in a dilemma.

'You are making an awkward request, Thetis,' he said with a sigh. 'You must know that Hera, my wife, has set her heart on the Greeks doing well in this war. She cannot forget that Paris failed to give her the apple destined for the most beautiful goddess. So she wants him and his family to be punished. As it is she suspects me of secretly siding with the Trojans. And now you come asking me to grant them successes in the war. I know I owe you a favour so I don't want to disappoint you. I expect you noticed that I have just nodded my agreement but I beg you, this must remain strictly between you and me. I will find a way of granting your wish, but leave now — don't let Hera see us together!'

'Thank you so much, Zeus,' answered Thetis, overjoyed, and she swiftly returned to the sea. The Olympians, including the mighty goddess Hera, were gathering around Zeus's golden throne.

No sooner had she sat down on the throne next to her husband than Hera gave him a suspicious look. 'Well, who has been here, Zeus, and what were you discussing with her behind my back? Are you plotting something else that I am not supposed to know about?' she said.

'Hera, you can't expect me to tell you about every step I make and every thought that occurs to me!' retorted Zeus with a frown. 'If it concerns you, you will know about it soon enough, but you can't go on asking questions and trying to spy on me all the time!'

'I stopped doing that long ago,' replied Hera. 'Anyway, you will always do as you please, you are always hiding something from me! However, I caught a glimpse of Thetis here on Mount Olympus. She asked something of you, didn't she?'

'You really are unbearable, Hera!' cried Zeus. 'Now I am beginning to dislike you. Either you obey my orders, or I will turn upon you in such a way that none of the gods will be able to help you. You know what I am like when I am really angry.'

With these words of warning, Zeus stood up, raised his right hand and sent out a flash of lightning so crushing that the whole earth quaked. At this, Hephaistos, the god of fire and blacksmith and armourer of all the Olympians, rushed to his mother's side and tried to persuade her:

'Stop getting excited, mother, and stop irritating Zeus. You know he is so powerful that he could easily send us down from our seats to the earth among the mortals. Anyway, we have come to his magnificent palace to amuse ourselves and enjoy the delights of good food and drink in a pleasant atmosphere. We can hardly wait for beautiful

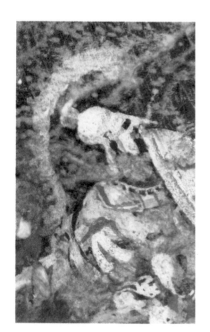

Ganymede and rosy-cheeked Hebe to serve us with ambrosia and nectar, our delicious food and drink. Give Zeus a pleasant smile, say something flattering to put him in a good mood and don't spoil our enjoyment at the feast.'

'Well, all right,' said Hera, her lips pressed together. When Hephaistos handed her a goblet filled with nectar, she forced a smile, but promised herself to settle the business with her faithless husband some other time. Now was not the right time.

Far into the night, the gods enjoyed themselves talking, dancing and singing. At last, when they were exhausted, they lay down on comfortable beds and were lulled to sleep by the sweet-sounding songs of the Muses.

Zeus didn't sleep a wink all night as he kept wondering how to fulfil the promise he had given to Achilles's mother. Suddenly a smile of relief appeared on his serious face. He had worked out a way of making the Greeks do something that would prove that they could achieve nothing without Thetis's son. Hypnos, the god of sleep, would enter Agamemnon's dreams disguised as Nestor, and would deceive him by declaring that the Olympian gods' favour was no longer divided between the Greeks and the Trojans and that Hera had won all of them over to the Greek side. He would also persuade him that the right moment for taking the city by storm had arrived.

Zeus immediately called Hypnos to him and asked him to carry out his instructions at once.

THE TEST

King Agamemnon woke up early in the morning, but for a long time he felt dazed by the strange dream he had had. Who was it that had looked so familiar to him? He had caught only a vague glimpse of the figure bending over his bed, but his face was like Nestor's, King of Pylos. It was also Nestor's voice speaking in a dignified and serious way. He felt as if he could still hear him: 'Agamemnon, it is time to call the armies together and to prepare for battle. Hera has won over all the gods to her side. Those who were on Priam's side have deserted him. Now you could conquer Troy and could take the city — that is the message sent by Zeus!'

At last, good news after nine long years! This would give encouragement to an army exhausted by so many years of unsuccessful fighting. Delighted with the news, Agamemnon sat up in bed, got dressed, collected his sword and sceptre, the sign of his royal power, and stepped out of his tent.

The camp was waking up slowly. Agamemnon ordered the sentries and guards to call all the leaders together as quickly as possible to King Nestor's ship. Agamemnon wanted to tell the Greek commanders about the message he had had from Zeus.

When they were gathered, the leaders listened to what Agamemnon had to say. Nestor replied on behalf of them all.

'If anyone else had told us such a story,' he declared, 'we would accuse him of trying to make fools of us. However, as it was you, Agamemnon, who had such a dream, it must have been sent by the gods, and must be true. If the gods are not on the Trojans' side, let us gather our troops and prepare to fight at once. We must call together all our warriors, from archers to charioteers, and decide jointly on a war plan as soon as we can.'

'All right, we will do what you suggest,' agreed Agamemnon. 'However, before we send the men to fight, let us see how high their spirits are because we've been at the camp for a long time and they may not be in the mood for fighting. Tell the men to

assemble on the main grounds of the camp.'

In a few moments, the camp was like a hive of buzzing bees. The men converged from the tents, from the seashore and from the ships. They looked impatient, amazed and excited. When the huge crowd had gathered in front of Agamemnon, he lifted his sceptre and spoke in a loud voice:

'Greek warriors, listen to what I have to say to you. For nine long years you have fought well, there is no denying that. Had it not been for their many allies, the Trojans could not have resisted for such a long time. But Zeus, who had promised us that after nine years we would conquer the city, is no longer willing to keep that promise. Yet it would be a disgrace to return home without a victory over Troy. But how can we overcome Troy when the signs are not in our favour? Wouldn't it be better to go back to our ships and return home to wait for a more favourable time?'

Agamemnon went silent, lifted his royal sceptre and looked around at the whole assembly.

He had expected them to disagree with his last suggestion and for them to accuse him of being a coward. He would have loved to have heard such words, but when he heard their cheering, he was astonished.

'Yes, yes, let's go home. Let us launch our ships. Let us hurry away from here as fast as we can. Back to Phocis! Back to Pylos! To Ithaka! To Argos!'

The enthusiastic roar spread across the whole assembly area. The crowd moved suddenly and the warriors started rushing head over heels to their ships as if they wanted to set sail before another day passed.

Agamemnon stood like a statue and just stared at the frenzied stampede, stiff and unable to utter a single word. Luckily, Odysseus was standing at his side.

'Do you mean to say that we are to leave Helen in Priam's kingdom for ever? When we have already sacrificed such a lot, are we suddenly to run away? Are we a handful of weak men, scared of the Trojans and their allies?' he exclaimed and tore the royal sceptre from Agamemnon's hand.

Without waiting, he dived in among the warriors who were rushing back to the ships drawn up on the mainland, caught some by the arms, pulled them back and, beating about him with the sceptre, yelled, 'You must have gone mad, all of you! Do you want to show your Commander-in-Chief, who is only trying to test your courage and determination that you are cowards? Don't you realize that you will be punished for such behaviour? Come back and listen to what the true intentions are.'

At these words, the crowd hesitated, and one by one, they began to turn back and sit down in front of their leader, ashamed of themselves.

But one of them, called Thersites, an ugly man with a squint, turned directly on Agamemnon: 'Do we have to listen to the same? What are you going to sing to us this time, Agamemnon? You will probably send us back to the fight because you have not got enough prizes. You've already got chests of gold; we have to

give you a part of our prizes after every expedition — and a slave girl, too! I suppose you think it would really be something to get hold of a Trojan prince. Someone should take him prisoner so that you can demand vast amounts of gold for his safe return. I say, friends and fellow soldiers, let's return home and let him stay here and command the stones on the hillside! Don't forget, Agamemnon did not hesitate in dishonouring even Achilles, who is a much better soldier than he is, and robbed him of Briseïs!'

'You filthy loud-mouth,' Odysseus retorted, 'those wisecracks of yours are the limit. You see badness in everybody else, although you yourself are certainly no hero. None of us knows which way the fortunes of war will turn, but this is no way to talk just before the decisive encounter! If you say such things again, I will give you a real beating.'

With these words Odysseus hit Thersites so hard that he bruised his back and brought tears to his eyes. The ugly fellow staggered and fell to the ground. The

soldiers all laughed — indeed
Thersites was nobody's favourite.
He was a great talker and
nobody was spared the rough
side of his tongue.

Meanwhile, Odysseus
continued, 'Maybe there are
others who have the same
opinion as Thersites. You may
hold it against Agamemnon that
we always seem to be fighting
Troy, but don't forget we have
promised always to support
Agamemnon, in good times and
in bad. It is certainly not easy for
you to be away from your wives,
your children and your homes for
such a long time. But it would be
a shame to have been on such
a long expedition and to return
home empty-handed. All of you
saw the sign at the altar in Aulis
when the snake strangled the
nine birds. And you know what
Calchas said that it meant. We
should carry on fighting until this
tenth year, which is certain to
fulfil everything promised by the
gods, and when the city of Troy,
with all its riches, will fall into our
hands. That day is now close
and we must do our best.'

Sometimes people can behave

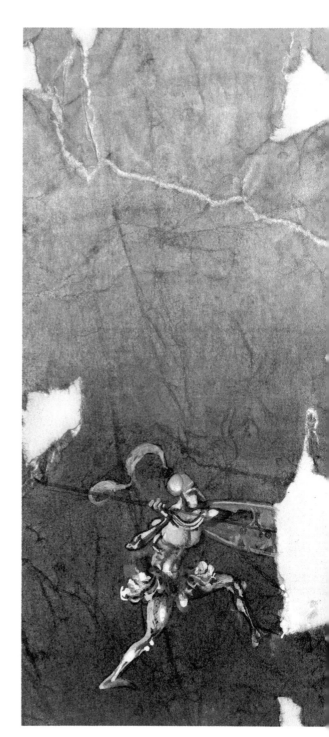

in very strange ways and change
their minds and moods very fast.
Only moments before the Greek
soldiers greeted Agamemnon
with enthusiastic cheering when
they thought he was sending
them home and now that
Odysseus was urging them
just as strongly to stay, they
were cheering and clapping
him.

In the wide valley of the
Scamander river, at the place
where sacrifices are made, the
warriors reformed in their ranks
and then stood in front of
Agamemnon and the other
leaders. A fat bull was placed on
the altar as an offering to Zeus
and the sacrificial ritual began.
They offered wine to Zeus and
the other gods and the festival
lasted all day, until at last
Agamemnon ended it with a
prayer to Zeus:

'Most famous, honoured ruler,
stronger than the other gods,
help us to bring down the walls
of Troy. Let us demolish Priam's
palace and help us to punish the
treacherous Paris. Help us to do
it before sunset tomorrow. We
are prepared for battle and shall

not give up until Troy has been flattened.'

There was thunderous applause and Pallas Athene was pleased with what she saw and filled the Greeks' hearts with courage. There was a glittering of shields, a flashing of armour and a magnificent display of spear-heads and swords.

But the most magnificent of all weapons, which inspired terror in the heart of any enemy, was missing among those ranks of warriors and heroes. For Achilles was not there. He was sitting idly in front of his tent, while his faithful Myrmidons amused themselves with archery and throwing contests.

A DUEL

While the Greeks were preparing for the fight, Iris, the winged messenger of the gods, went down to the city of Troy at Zeus's request. The Assembly was in session at the royal palace and news of the intending attack was brought to the assembled leaders by Polites, one of King Priam's sons:

'Hector, there are as many men as there are sands in the seashore or leaves in the forest. There is no time to lose. You must sound the alarm immediately and every man who can fight must do so.'

The message was so alarming that Hector, Priam's eldest son, who was the chief defence commander, didn't waste one moment. He immediately suspended the assembly, put on his helmet and began to issue orders:

'Hurry and put double sentries at the approaches to the walls. Hitch the horses to the chariots and drive them out on to the plain. Form ranks and stick together so that you can support each other.'

Hector behaved like a true leader. He rode around the detachments of the army, pointed out their positions in the field, encouraged the timid men and calmed down the over-enthusiastic ones.

After the Trojans and their allied forces had been positioned in sight of the Greeks, there was a tense silence. The men gripped their swords or pressed the handles of their hatchets, the archers bent the bowstrings, while the lancers had their spears at the ready.

The two armies were about to clash when, all of a sudden, Paris stepped out from the Trojan ranks, wearing a panther-skin cloak, and with his sword at his side and a bronze-headed spear in each hand, he shouted at the Greeks:

'Here I am, King Priam's son, the reason why you want to storm our rich city! Do you think that you have scared us by camping out on the plain in such overwhelming numbers? We have been waiting patiently. You have never subdued us before and you will never subdue us now. It is a shame that there is no one in

your ranks brave enough to meet
me in a hand-to-hand fight.
I would like the challenge.'

A shudder went through the
rows of Greek soldiers. The next
moment, King Menelaus came
riding out in front of the armies
in his war chariot. He jumped
down, drew his sword and waved
it above his head:

'Well, here I am, Paris, I the

A DUEL

true husband of the woman you took away as you abused our hospitality. If you want to fight, don't hesitate. My sword can't wait to pierce your chest and to carry out my revenge!'

Perhaps it was because the sword flashed so brightly in the sun or perhaps it was because Menelaus answered his challenge so quickly, but Paris suddenly lost heart. He turned pale in the face, put his spears in the ground and started backing towards his Trojans. However, he didn't go far. After he had taken only a few steps, his brother Hector grasped his shoulder and told him off.

'What do you think you are doing, Paris? You silly show-off! Haven't you any pride? Can't you hear them laughing at you? They regarded you as a heroic fighter, a brave man, and now they can see that you have not even the courage to face the man whose wife you took away. So many people have had to suffer because of what you did, but you yourself are not willing to risk your own skin!' he said.

Paris sighed, and bowed his

head sadly: 'Hector, I know you are right in many ways, but it is not my fault that Aphrodite has granted me her favour, indeed, beauty is the gift of the gods. However, I don't want to ruin our family's reputation — if you think I should accept Menelaus's challenge, I will. Whoever wins will keep Helen as well as her jewels and riches. However, if I fight Menelaus on his own, the Greeks, and of course our own men, must put away their weapons. When the fight has been won, everyone can go away peacefully.'

'At last you have said something sensible,' said Hector. 'I will send negotiators to Agamemnon and will ask our father, Priam, to agree to the duel.'

At that time, Priam was staying at the tower with a group of noblemen who were too old to fight. The King had invited Helen into the tower to watch the battle and point out the different Greek leaders. Although they were old, the sight of Helen made them young again. She was so beautiful and charming that they

63

found nothing strange in the fact
that it was because of her that such
terrible fighting had been raging
for such a long time. Even Priam
himself was not concerned that his
kingdom had been flung into
a bloody war. He put it all down to
the interference of the gods. When
Hector's messengers asked for his
consent to Paris's duel with
Menelaus, he believed that the

A DUEL

gods were even involved in this.

'Menelaus wants to fight to save the Greeks from a blood bath. In that case, Paris must not fail or he would dishonour the whole of our family,' Priam decided on hearing Hector's message. 'All right,' he resolved. 'Let us agree that no one will interfere in this duel. Only the two of them shall meet on the plains outside the city walls. Only their spears shall determine who will eventually possess Helen. I will agree to the outcome, although I have already become fond of her as my dear daughter-in-law. But now harness the horses; I will drive to the battlefield to meet Agamemnon. We shall honour the agreement with a sacrifice of lambs. Then I will return to my palace — I am old, and no longer have the strength to watch my youngest son fighting for his life.'

Priam left to meet Agamemnon, who was waiting for him in an open space between the two armies accompanied by Odysseus.

The Kings greeted each other politely and they were led to the altar where the burnt offerings were ready. Addressing the warriors on both sides Agamemnon exclaimed, 'Glorious Zeus and all you eternal gods, witness our promises. Let the duel take place. If anyone breaks the agreement, he must be punished and so must his wife and children, too.'

Then Priam repeated the words of this solemn promise and so did the noblemen on both sides.

When the sacrifice had finished, Hector and Odysseus started to measure out the ground between the two armies where the duel was to take place. A draw took place to see who was to throw first. Paris won. He would be the first to fling his spear at his opponent.

Paris started to prepare for the fight straight away. Armour to protect his shins was tied at the ankles with silver clips. Then he put on armour to protect his body, collected his silver-hilted sword and slung a massive bronze shield over his left arm. Finally he put on his helmet and took his spear in his right hand.

As he looked up, he saw Menelaus fastening the last strap on the chin-piece of his helmet.

Paris raised his spear and slowly walked to the appointed place. Menelaus approached him brandishing his weapon. Each of them had an overwhelming desire to kill his opponent and a cruel hatred flashed from their eyes. It was a terrifying sight for those following them at a distance.

Suddenly, Paris stopped, leaned back to put his full weight behind his weapon, and his spear whizzed through the air and landed heavily on Menelaus's shield. But the bronze spear did not penetrate the shield. Its point was bent back and the weapon slid down to Menelaus's feet.

Now it was Menelaus's turn to use his spear. He, too, balanced it in his hand, and prayed to Zeus for success. Then with a cry, he raised his arm and hurled the spear with such force that it pierced the Trojan's shield and glittering armour. It tore through the side of Paris's tunic and Paris just managed to avoid being killed by moving at the last moment. Menelaus then attacked him with his sword, holding it in both hands and bringing it down on Paris's helmet with such force that the sword broke into half a dozen pieces. The Trojan prince staggered and fell forward on to the ground. Menelaus hurled himself at Paris, seized him by the helmet, tied the helmet strap under his chin so tight it cut into his throat and began to drag him triumphantly to the Greeks.

Paris struggled in vain, panting for breath, coughing and wheezing. He would certainly have died if the goddess Aphrodite hadn't come to his help. At the last moment she broke the tightening strap and Menelaus was left with the empty helmet in his hand. He threw it aside and flung himself again at Paris determined to get his revenge. However, Aphrodite had no intention of leaving her protégé unprotected. She hid Paris in a veil of black mist, carried him away and laid him down on the bed in Helen's bedroom. Then she disguised herself as an old wool worker and went to fetch Helen. She was still in the high tower watching the duel on the plain.

'Paris is calling for you, Helen. Go and see him in your room. He wants to speak to you. Hurry up, he is waiting for you,' she said.

Helen quickly went to the royal palace but she was not very happy. She had not completely forgotten the years spent in Sparta and though she went willingly to Troy, she began to wonder whether she had made the right decision.

As those thoughts went through her mind, she saw Paris

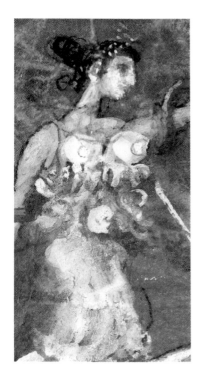

on the bed. She saw him lifting his arms towards her and she looked away:

'So, you are back from the battlefield, Paris! I was hoping you might have been killed. You used to boast that you were tough, that Menelaus could not match you in anything, and now you have crept home like a mouse. You were holding your fine head a bit too high! Next time, don't challenge Menelaus to a duel, or you may fall on his spear!'

'Helen, you really do insult me!' Paris replied. 'No doubt Menelaus was helped by Pallas Athene. She is sure to have helped his spear to pierce both my shield and my armour and put the brakes on mine!

Fortunately there are also gods on our side, otherwise I could not have survived that unequal fight. Next time, I will win with their help. But, Helen, please stand by me. You must help me first with your love — you know how much you mean to me.'

'Oh Paris, Paris,' Helen whispered, falling into his arms. 'You are the only one for whom my heart burns.'

While they sank into each other's arms, Menelaus was searching in vain for his vanished rival. From the moment the dark cloud covered him, no one had had even a glimpse of the Trojan Prince. But as Paris had disappeared, didn't that make Menelaus the winner?

A DUEL

'My brother has beaten Paris
in a duel. You saw it, my dear
Greeks, as you Trojans did, even
you who are the allies of both
sides!' thundered Agamemnon at
last. 'Menelaus has overcome the
man who took away his wife and
according to the agreement you
have made, Helen belongs to him
again, along with all her riches.
We must receive compensation
for the fighting against Troy!
We mustn't interfere for this
seems to be the will of the gods!'

The Greeks were delighted to
hear the King's words, but the
Trojans were embarrassed.
However, neither suspected that
the gods wanted events to work
out differently, and that on Mount
Olympus their motives had just
given rise to a renewed quarrel.

THE ARROW
OF PANDARUS

In Zeus's palace on Mount Olympus, the gods were having a feast. As usual, the charming Hebe poured sweet nectar into the golden tankards, and the guests cheerfully drank from them. Only now and then, one of them cast a look down on to the plain of Troy. Zeus was once again in a sarcastic mood and began to play a trick on his wife, Hera.

'That man Menelaus is an unfortunate beggar,' he sneered.

'The powerful goddesses, Hera and Pallas Athene, are on his side, but they seem happy to sit around on Mount Olympus while Aphrodite shields Paris from disaster. And what can we do about it now? Should we acknowledge Menelaus as the winner? Perhaps it will be better to let him take Helen back to Sparta and let Troy live in peace.'

Hera and Pallas Athene were sitting together near Zeus's golden throne with a worried

look on their faces. Pallas Athene did not dare to challenge her father, but Hera burst out at once: 'I will not stand for this, Zeus! I took such a lot of trouble to gather many Greek clans to make difficulties for Priam, and now you just stand up and say, "Let Menelaus take Helen back, and let everything remain just as it used to be." I will never put up with this.'

'Hera, in your hatred you would prefer Priam to be destroyed, but I have nothing against him. He honours me and sacrifices many animals and a lot of wine to me — why should I want Troy to be destroyed?' Zeus replied.

'Because I am also a goddess, because Kronos is my father as well as yours and because I was offended not only as a woman but also as your divine wife. You must recognize that they must be punished. You shall tell Pallas Athene to descend to earth and make plans for the Trojans to break the truce. Then the Greeks will attack them. You will soon see if Pallas Athene and I are content to be idle and just look down from Olympus,' Hera responded.

'What am I to do with you?… have it your own way,' said Zeus with a sigh. 'I know how difficult you will be to live with if you don't get your own way. Pallas Athene, go to the plain of Troy and do what is necessary.'

Zeus didn't have to tell Pallas Athene twice. Like a comet with a sparkling tail, she flashed down to earth (all the men in the camp took this as a bad sign), disguised herself as Laodocus, Antenor's son, and looked for

Pandarus, the Trojans' famous archer.

'Listen, Pandarus, we simply cannot allow Menelaus to take Helen away,' she insinuated to him. 'Paris won't stand for it. Why don't you try to do away with Menelaus? Paris will be very grateful to you. One well-aimed arrow can solve everything. Just look, Menelaus is running around the battlefield without noticing what is going on around him. If you wait for him, properly hidden, no one will even know where the arrow came from. You will save Troy from disgrace – and at home you will be treated as a hero.'

Pandarus was flattered by these words as he was very keen to become a hero. He took his goatshorn bow, chose a new arrow and asked four of his armed comrades to protect him with their shields. Then he waited for Menelaus to appear. Pandarus held the bow-string close to his chest until he had a clear view of Menelaus.

Pandarus let the arrow fly. It hit Menelaus, penetrating his decorated belt. Pandarus had aimed very well but, of course, Pallas Athene did not want the wound to kill Menelaus. The point of the arrow only scratched Menelaus's skin. Even so, a stream of blood poured from the cut and Menelaus's thigh was stained red.

Agamemnon, who was standing nearby, was aghast. He realized that blood had been shed after a sacrifice had been offered to the gods and an agreement made that all weapons would be laid aside.

'Dear King, my brother Menelaus, the Trojans will be sorry for this trick,' cried the King of Mycenae, his voice faltering with anger. 'Oh, what wickedness, what treachery! Priam must be killed. Troy must be wiped from the face of the earth. Oh, brother, you are still bleeding. I will send Machaon, the doctor, to you; he will help you. Talthybius, go and fetch him here at once; you can see how Menelaus is suffering!'

Agamemnon was wild with rage, ranting and raving until the wounded Menelaus himself calmed him down:

'Perhaps it will not be so bad after all, dear brother. Don't look so horrified! I think my metal belt caught the point of the arrow so that it did not hit a vital organ. Calm down, and tell our allies what has happened. There will soon be another fight. Tell them to get ready! Look, here is Machaon coming!'

The famous doctor, who was said to have learned his skills from the centaur Cheiron, examined the King's wound

carefully, extracted the arrow and applied a soothing ointment. Menelaus felt better immediately. He sat up and watched the preparations in the Greek camp.

The Greeks began to get ready to fight. Agamemnon rode in his war chariot from one rank to another, encouraging the men and issuing battle orders.

'Don't be frightened, brave Greeks!' he cried, brandishing his sword. 'The Trojans, like the villains they are, have gone back on their word, and you know very well that as they are the ones who cheated, they will never win the favour of Zeus. The opposite will happen: he always punishes anyone who breaks his promise. So let the Trojans get what they deserve for their treachery. Prepare for battle, don't just stand there. Rush against the Trojans now and force them to run away.'

Thus he urged on the Greek troops. The soldiers felt their hearts beating faster and drumming in their ears. The Greek ranks lined up, one formation joined the other in battle order. They rushed forward like the waves in the sea, on and on, without a murmur, without a shout.

Facing them, like a gigantic wall, rose the lines of Trojan armour-bearers. The shields of Priam's army glittered, the bows trembled. Bare swords and spear points were aimed against the advancing Greeks, and from the throats of the Trojans and their allies a horrible roar went up across the whole plain, as if a herd of bulls had started roaring. The fighting had started.

An arrow sent out by an impatient archer whizzed through the air. There was a clear clang of metal as swords clashed; a helmet fell into the dust of the battlefield. The first fighter crushed his opponent's ribs with his foot. A wounded horse jibbed and neighed. Charioteers were falling from their chariots onto the dusty plain.

Soon the first victims of the savage fighting lay on the ground outside Troy. How that place had changed since the occasion when Priam and Agamemnon pledged their word not to interfere with weapons in the duel between the King of Sparta and the Prince of Troy!

The number of victims was so high that even Hector was alarmed and considered withdrawing. After being reminded by Apollo, he realized that the Greeks were actually fighting without Achilles, and that he should not lose heart and should keep up the fight.

Similarly, Pallas Athene inspired the Greeks' fight and they were just as keen as the Trojans in battle.

The armies attacked each other so desperately that there were huge numbers of dead bodies all over the plain but the end of the fighting was not yet in sight.

DIOMEDES AND THE INTERVENTION OF THE GODDESSES

DIOMEDES AND THE INTERVENTION
OF THE GODDESSES

The first hours of the fighting passed, but neither side had won any real advantage. The attacks came first from one side, then the other. A rank which had gained a piece of ground soon lost it, and those who had fallen back soon recovered their former position. The fiercest fighter was Diomedes, King of Argos.

This Greek hero frightened all the Trojans. Only Aeneas, who had brought troops from Dardania, was not overawed by him. In the fighting, he kept close to Pandarus, and urged him every now and then by saying, 'Pandarus, we must do something about taming that man Diomedes. You are our best archer. See if you can wound him with your arrows.'

'I have already tried, Aeneas. I aimed an arrow at him and I thought that it hit him in the right shoulder, but it seemed only to scratch him. One of the gods must be protecting him.'

'The main thing is not to give up, Pandarus. Get into my chariot and I will ride as close as possible to Diomedes and you take a good, close aim at him.

Or would you prefer to drive the chariot and leave it to me to attack Diomedes with my spear?'

'No, no, Aeneas, the horses are used to you. Just drive them so that we can get as close to him as possible. Diomedes is sure to attack us and that will be the right opportunity for me. He shall not live to see the sun set!'

Diomedes was warned of the approaching chariot by his friend Sthenelus.

'Pandarus and Aeneas are rushing at us,' he warned the King of Argos. 'They are the most dangerous fighters, so we must be extra careful. Do not forget that the goddess Aphrodite is Aeneas's mother. Perhaps we ought to move back; it is not always an advantage to fight in the front line.'

Diomedes would not hear of any such retreat. 'To move back… you might as well say run away,' he said angrily. 'I am not used to fighting at the back. Are they coming at us in a chariot? In that case, I will stand up to them on my own legs!'

All at once, a high cloud of dust rose before him, blown up

by the wheels of the racing chariot. Pandarus was on it next to Aeneas, shouting and brandishing his spear: 'You escaped my arrow, Diomedes, but you won't escape my spear. This time I will be more precise.'

He hurled his spear so forcefully that the metal point went right through Diomedes's small shield and was stopped only by his body armour. Diomedes staggered but did not fall. He cried out, swung his arm forcefully and flung his spear towards Pandarus, putting all his strength into the throw.

Pandarus groaned with pain, groped for the spear, which had dug right into the middle of his forehead, and fainted. He fell from the chariot, dead.

The Greeks gave out a victorious war-cry across the battlefield. Aeneas was horrified. His legs momentarily turned to stone. The thought flashed through his mind that the Greeks could take Pandarus's body, drag it away, and strip it of his armour. He didn't want this to happen, so he rushed forward to protect his dead companion from

such a fate. Aeneas stood over his friend's body, protected him with his round shield and was ready to kill anyone who came near, when suddenly he saw Diomedes.

He was carrying a giant stone, a piece of rock so big that three ordinary men could hardly lift it. He was panting and coming slowly towards Aeneas. Aeneas instantly held out his shield to protect him, but then Diomedes stopped, stretched his legs, swung the immense stone over his head and flung it with an almighty force. Aeneas felt an unbearable pain in his hip. He sank to his knees and tried to support himself with one hand on the ground, but the pain in his hip was too severe. Everything went black before his eyes and the Dardanean leader collapsed in a dead faint.

He would certainly have died there and then if his divine mother, the goddess Aphrodite, had not rushed to his aid. She threw her arms around her son, hid him under her shimmering robe to protect him from the flying weapons and, carrying him

in her arms, ran from the battlefield.

However, while Sthenelus took away Aeneas's chariot and horses as war prizes to the Greek camp, Diomedes, carrying his spear, went in relentless pursuit of the fleeing Aphrodite. Why should Aeneas escape from him at the last moment when he had staked his own life in the fight? He chased the goddess through the ranks of soldiers and, as he got within ten steps of her, he hurled his spear. The metal tip tore her robe and pierced her wrist. The goddess cried out and she dropped her precious burden.

But even then, Diomedes didn't succeed in getting hold of Aeneas. Apollo, who favoured the Trojans, happened to be watching how his protégés were doing. When he saw that the Dardanean leader, Aeneas, had been driven into a tight corner, he took Aphrodite's place and swiftly intervened. He covered Aeneas with a thick, dark cloud and prepared to carry the wounded hero away from the battleground. Doing so, he called out to Aphrodite, 'Leave the battlefield,

daughter of Zeus. This is not the place for you. Go and find your brother Ares, the god of war, who is having fun here. Ask him to lend you his swift horses to take you up to Olympus. Don't worry any more about Aeneas. I will bring him to my temple in Troy and heal him there. I am on the side of the Trojans myself just as you are.'

Aphrodite was pleased to hear Apollo's words and when she arrived at Mount Olympus, she fell into her mother's arms.

'My child, my dear child, what are these tears for? And how did you get that wound? Let me put some soothing ointment on your wrist,' said Dione.

'This is all Diomedes's fault. He wounded me as I was trying to rescue Aeneas from the battlefield. What is more natural than for a mother to want to save her son's life? The horrible Greeks are not just waging war with the Trojans, they have the nerve to fight the immortal gods too,' Aphrodite complained right in front of Zeus's throne.

'I understand, dear, but this is not the first time that a mortal

DIOMEDES AND THE INTERVENTION OF THE GODDESSES

has injured a god,' said Dione with a sigh. 'You must not take it so much to heart. Look, your wound is already healing; before long you will have forgotten all about it. And Diomedes's turn will come.'

Hera looked on with a wicked smile as Dione treated her daughter's injury, and felt secretly glad that Aphrodite had been taught a lesson. Pallas Athene, standing, as usual, close to her father's throne, made a nasty remark.

'I hope you don't mind my saying,' she said turning to Zeus, 'but I believe that your Cyprian daughter must have aided and abetted some love affairs between the Trojans and the Greek girls – and the scratch on her hand is something she has richly deserved.'

Zeus gave a little smile and covered his mouth with his hand. He said, 'Aphrodite, Aphrodite! Why are you meddling in military affairs? That is not your business, you should be in charge of love and marriage. Battles and wars are the concern of Ares and Pallas Athene. Leave well alone.'

'As a matter of fact, Ares is already storming around on the plain in front of Troy!' rejoined Pallas Athene. 'Just look, father. He has disguised himself as the Thracian hero, Acamas, driven back Diomedes with the help of Hector and is gathering the Trojans for a wild attack on the Greek camp. Apollo even went so far as to heal Aeneas miraculously and to send him back among the Trojans to encourage them to keep fighting. Look, the battle is about to rage again!'

The words of the goddess were true. Zeus looked down at a terrible sight. Once again, weapons were clashing and clanging, one blow followed by another, much blood was being spilled and there were many deaths on both sides.

The Greeks were the first to start losing their strength. But as they began to withdraw from the battlefield, the goddess Hera intervened from the heights of Mount Olympus. 'Athene, now it is up to us two to interfere in the fighting. We cannot allow Ares to create any more havoc,' she

exclaimed and at once rounded upon her husband Zeus.

'Don't you think that Ares has gone too far? I am the greatest goddess and I have promised Menelaus that the offence against him will be punished. And now Ares is doing his best to have Menelaus's men killed. I hope you won't be angry with me if I chase him out of Troy.'

'It is entirely up to you, Hera,' said the ruler of Olympus. 'You know I am not particularly fond of Ares. Do whatever you think is best. And take Pallas Athene with you. She will be only too pleased to help you.'

Both goddesses immediately set out to help the Greeks. Pallas Athene harnessed the horses which pulled her heavy chariot. It had golden and bronze wheels and was made of gold and silver. Hera took the reins. Pallas Athene put on her tunic and armed herself with a shield. Then she put on her four-crested helmet and gripping her spear, stepped into the gleaming chariot.

Hera flicked the horses with her whip and they galloped through the gates of Olympus, through the clouds and down to the earth to the plain in front of Troy.

There was Diomedes's chariot by the river bank. Diomedes was nearby wiping the blood from the wound caused by Pandarus's arrow and cooling it in the waters of the Scamander river.

'What are you doing here?' Pallas Athene asked him. 'Have you stopped fighting the Trojans? Are you tired of the fighting? Or are you frightened? Don't you believe that I can help you?'

Diomedes looked up and stopped treating his wound. He recognized Pallas Athene and rejected her harsh words: 'I am certainly not frightened, goddess, and I know that you have been on our side. Nor do I feel tired. I am holding back because the Trojans are being led against us by the wicked Ares.'

'Do not be afraid of him. I shall sort him out — with your help, if only because he does not know how to keep his word. He promised both Hera and myself that he would support the Greek

cause and now, all of a sudden, he has joined the other side. Hand me the reins; you are driving to the battlefield with me.'

She jumped onto the chariot, put on Hades's helmet, which made her invisible, and spurred on the team of horses. They were rushing like the wind and Ares saw them when they were quite near. Straightaway, he launched at Diomedes with his spear. However, Pallas Athene caught the shaft in her hand and made it swerve so that it missed him. 'Now it is your turn!' she cried, and Diomedes, following her instruction, raised his spear. It whizzed through the air and the goddess drove it so that it struck Ares in his loins.

A thousand men could not have cried out as loudly as Ares did. At that moment both the Trojan and Greek ranks shuddered with horror. A huge column of a black cloud rose up in which Ares shrouded himself from head to foot to whirl straight up to the seat of Zeus.

'Ruler of gods and kings, did you see what happened? A mortal dared to attack a member of the immortal Olympian family,' he whimpered before Zeus. 'That was the work of Pallas Athene, I know, but is she allowed to do things like that? Perhaps you ought to tell her off instead of forgiving her for everything she does.'

'Do not come to me and whine,' Zeus stopped him. 'You

enjoy nothing more than starting a quarrel and a fight, but no one is allowed even to touch you. If you were not my own flesh and blood I would have been delighted to send you to my brother, Hades, into the underworld. Let Paieon, our doctor, put on some soothing ointment and Hebe will prepare a bath for you!'

Ares, trying not to cry out, retreated in silence, while Zeus turned on his golden throne and looked down on the plain of Troy.

Hera and Pallas Athene were already flying back to Olympus. The ranks of the Trojans and their allies began to hesitate and withdraw slowly back to the walls.

PARTING WITH ANDROMACHE

Soon after Ares and the two goddesses had left the battleground, a crowd of Trojan women gathered in front of Priam's palace. The city was full of alarming reports that the Greeks had braced themselves for a counterattack and that the defenders were being pushed near to the city walls. The mothers, wives and daughters of the soldiers were very worried. What was happening on the plain? How were those who had left to defend Troy getting on? What would happen next if the Greeks were not beaten? It was rumoured that, without Achilles, the Greeks could achieve nothing. But Diomedes was proving to be equally as terrifying as Achilles. Trojan women rushed to the palace as they had heard that Hector had come with fresh news about how the battle was going.

As soon as they saw the royal prince, they realized how bitter

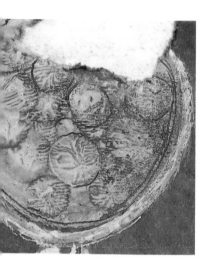

the fighting was. There were bloodstains on his shield and shin guards, his brow was covered with beads of sweat and his beard and forehead were covered with dust from the battle. But his helmet and spear were still shining.

When Hecabe, Hector's mother, appeared from Priam's palace, she had a real shock. Hector looked older and very worried. She rushed to her son, held on to his arm, and spoke to him with great anxiety:

'Hector, my brave son, what is the matter? Something awful will surely happen now that you have left the battlefield. We can do nothing else but turn to the gods, to Zeus himself, to help us hold back the Greeks. I am right, aren't I? Wait a moment while I fetch the wine. Offer some to Zeus and then you can drink some. It will refresh you and give you strength to carry on the fight.'

'No, no, mother, don't bring any wine,' Hector replied. 'Can't you see what I look like? Drenched in blood, covered in dirt and dust. I can't offer wine to the gods while I look like this. But, mother, go with the women of the royal family and the other wives and daughters who are here to the temple of Pallas Athene as quickly as you can. Each of you must take your best dress and lay it on the lap of the goddess's statue. Promise her that we will offer another rich sacrifice and pray to her to pity us, and above all to keep a close eye on Diomedes who is leading the Greeks and attacking our forces. Goodbye, mother, I must go and join Paris. I hope that he will join us again in the fight. After all, he is the cause of all our trouble!'

The Trojan women listened to his words with horror, but Hector took no notice of their despair. He left his mother and ran to Priam's palace. He went straight to the place where Paris lived. It was a magnificent building, constructed by the best workmen and filled with every luxury. Paris had always believed that not even the best was good enough for his Helen!

Hector found Paris in one of the ladies' rooms. Hector, spear

in hand and still bloodstained, came face to face with Paris just as he was admiring his shield. Helen and several ladies-in-waiting were weaving. Paris was calm and cheerful just as if there were no cruel battle raging underneath the walls. Hector's blood began to boil and he was beside himself with rage.

'Paris, what are you lounging around here for?' he fumed. 'Out on the plain, we are being mercilessly wounded, our wives and mothers are terrified and you have nothing better to do than to polish your shield and spear! It is your fault that this city is under siege. If anyone else were shirking his duty, you would be the first to attack him. Go into battle, Paris. Don't you care about the fate of Troy?'

Paris and Helen stared, horrified at what Hector had said.

'Hector, you are right,' said Paris, who was sorry and wanted to reassure his brother, 'but then again, not quite. I was just deciding what to do next. You know I am very worried at the awful things that are happening because of Helen. She herself has been urging me to return to the front, and as you see, I was actually just getting ready to do so. I will put on my armour now. Wait a moment, or else go on ahead; I will catch you up.'

Hector didn't reply but stared at Helen who hid her pretty face in her hands. She peeked out at him and moaned unhappily, 'Oh, brother, I am a shameless, beastly creature. I wish I hadn't been born. Why did I bring so much misery, so much suffering to overwhelm us? Why didn't the gods give me a braver husband? But don't be cross with Paris; you will never change him. That is why I am so concerned about what will happen to him. You are the bravest man I know. Here, sit down and rest. You must be awfully tired.'

'I can't, Helen, they are already expecting me on the battlefield. And I want to see my wife, Andromache, and my son for a while — who knows if I will survive the battle safe and sound? The gods may want the Greeks to kill me. Make sure that Paris finally goes to the battlefield. Let him join me as soon as he is ready.'

Hector couldn't find his wife in Priam's palace. At first, he thought Andromache had gone with Priam's daughters and her sisters-in-law to Athene's shrine to offer a sacrifice. Then he found the caretaker and asked him if this was so.

'No, my dear sir, you won't find her there,' he replied, looking worried. 'Your sisters and your brothers' wives asked her to come with them to Pallas Athene's temple, but the lady Andromache had just heard that our men were being worn down. She began crying and ordered the nurse to take care of your son Astyanax. All the time she was shouting that she must find out what was going on on the plain, and she rushed off like a madwoman.'

'To the city walls!' cried Hector. He rushed from the room and dashed through the streets of Troy, worried in case Andromache went beyond the walls to where the fighting was. He ran and elbowed his way through groups of women and girls hurrying towards Athene's shrine, overtook men who were hurrying to help

defend the city and passed many wounded soldiers, pushing aside the young boys who were hanging around in admiration of the heroes.

At last, near to the gate, he saw Andromache. She ran to meet him, closely followed by her maid who was carrying their son. The little boy was laughing breathlessly because he had enjoyed the wild ride in his nurse's arms. His eyes sparkled like stars. Hector drew a deep sigh of relief and took his wife and son in his arms. She hugged him with tears in her eyes.

'My dear, foolish Hector,' she whispered, 'your bravery will be the death of you. Why are you

always throwing yourself into battle? I am so frightened. I am afraid you will make our son an orphan and me a widow. I don't want to lose you. My father and my seven brothers have all been killed by Achilles. Don't rush to the front line; stay here on the tower and command the forces from here.'

Andromache burst into tears. Her last words were almost drowned by heartbreaking sobs. She was shaking like a leaf in Hector's arms.

'I understand you, Andromache,' said Hector soothingly. 'Don't think I have no feeling for you, but I would hate myself if I left the battle right now. I have trained myself to defend Troy in the front line, and I would be a coward to leave now. The day is coming when Troy will be destroyed and Priam and the people of Troy will be left in its ruins. But more than anything I am thinking of you. I keep picturing one of the Greek soldiers taking you as a part of his war prize. Instead of this lovely dress, you would wear rags, your bracelet would be

replaced by a broom and your crown by a rag in your hands. It is terrible to imagine, my dearest, the indifferent comments your future master might make about you. "Oh, that maid there?" he will say. "She used to be the wife of Hector, the Trojan hero." I would rather fall in battle than have to live to see such a scene!'

Hector fell silent and again stroked Andromache's hair. Then releasing her from his arms, he stepped towards his beloved little son. 'Astyanax, my dear child, come to your father for a while and let me give you a cuddle.'

The little boy looked at his father, and the stars sparkling in his eyes suddenly went out and the corners of his mouth turned down. The child shrank back wailing and buried his face in his nurse's shoulder.

'What's this, little one? I hope you're not frightened of my flashing helmet or its horsehair plume,' said Hector with a smile. 'Do you know what we shall do? We will take it off — look, I am taking it off now — putting it on the floor and I shall give you a hug!'

Astyanax calmed down, raised his arms towards his father and cuddled up to him. Hector was happy and covered him with kisses. He swung the little boy from one side to the other and even threw him high up over his head. Then he gave Astyanax to his mother and prayed to Zeus:

'Zeus of Olympus, great ruler of gods and kings, let my son become a strong and famous hero! Let him terrorize his enemies and do everything to make his mother happy. Let all the Trojan people be proud of him and say, "Here is a better man than his father!"'

Andromache smiled through her tears and for a brief moment, she was happy. For a second she forgot the fate given to her by the gods.

Once again, Hector stroked her hair and put his arm around her shoulders. 'Darling, there is no sense in distressing yourself. We can't change fate and if I am not destined to be killed in the battle, none of the Greek fighters can send me down to Hades's underground kingdom. But if it is my fate to be killed, then I will be

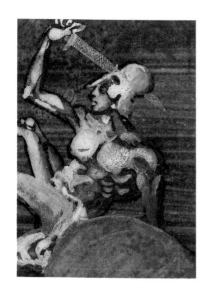

hit even here, on this fortified tower. Now stop thinking of the noise of the battle. Go home, get on with your work and look after our little one — just like you used to. Leave the war to us men.'

He kissed his wife goodbye and stroked his son's face. Then he waited until the two set out for home. Andromache walked slowly, trying not to cry, but as soon as she was back at the palace, she cried uncontrollably.

Hector walked back to the battlefield, proudly and like a real hero. Behind him, looking splendid in his shining armour, Paris was walking quickly.

ANOTHER DUEL

ANOTHER DUEL

While Hector and Paris were hurrying to the battlefield, Apollo and Pallas Athene met by the famous oak tree near the castle of Troy.

'There has been more than enough bloodshed today, I should think,' said Apollo, welcoming Athene. He was sure that the goddess had again sped down from Mount Olympus to urge the Greeks to fight more. 'Looking round the battleground, it seems to me that there are far too many victims for the first day of the fighting. What about letting both sides rest? Wait — let me finish — I know that you are prepared to help the Greeks win and I know Hera is also on their

side. But I hope not even she wants to see such butchery!'

'The goddesses are true to their word, Apollo,' replied Pallas Athene. 'Of course, if you have a good idea of how to put a stop to today's fighting, I will consider it.'

'Pallas Athene, you and Hera will eventually achieve your goal — that much is clear to me — but that is all the more reason why the slaughter should cease. What do you think about Hector fighting another duel? Let him challenge one of the Greeks. They will no doubt be surprised at such an idea, but they will certainly find an opponent. The winner will decide the victorious side of the encounter.'

'I agree,' answered Pallas Athene. 'If Hector gives his side a signal to stop the fighting, I will see to it that the Greeks do the same. When all the warriors put their weapons down, we will turn into vultures and watch the duel from the top of the sacred oak tree.'

So it was agreed that both sides should stop fighting and Pallas Athene made the Greeks take up Hector's challenge to a duel.

'Listen to me, Trojan soldiers, and you Greeks as well!' boomed Hector when both the Trojans and the Greeks had taken off their shields. 'I am speaking to you because I want to try and stop this fighting. Why should there be so many deaths? I am sure that there are a great many brave Greek heroes among you. If one of you volunteers to meet me in a duel, this will prevent dozens of men from destroying each other in a bloody encounter. But there is just one condition for myself and you: if I am killed in the fight, my armour must be given to my conqueror. However, he must not let my body be mutilated, but must take it to my wife to have it cremated. And if I win, I will do the same, whoever my opponent is. Will you accept my offer? Tell me, who is brave enough to meet me?'

The Greeks listened to Hector's speech in silence. No one was willing to reject him outright; this would have been degrading. And similarly, no one wanted to be ridiculous or denounced as a

coward. But it was even more difficult to volunteer to fight the tall, courageous Hector. Perhaps only one man was his equal — and that was Achilles.

Eventually, Menelaus took up his sword and spoke harshly to his comrades: 'I get the impression that there is no one among you who is willing to take up the challenge. You sit here like a flock of wet hens and leave it to me, a man with far less strength than Hector, to save our reputation. All right, since no one else has the courage, I will fight Hector myself!'

'Are you mad, brother?' cried Agamemnon. 'You do not even know what you are saying. You, who are much weaker, would be easy prey for Hector! Do you want to lose our struggle in such an unequal duel? Let me fight the Trojan.'

'Agamemnon is right,' King Nestor intervened, 'and my only regret is that I am no longer a young man. If I were, Hector would have found a true opponent.'

Perhaps the fact that the dignified old King of Pylos had spoken his mind, or perhaps a wave of shame over their long hesitation worked a change in the minds of the Greek commanders. Several of them stepped out of the line at the same moment and began to rattle their swords.

'I will fight,' Diomedes exclaimed, turning red in the face and lifting his spear high over his head. 'Agamemnon, you are the Commander-in-Chief; it is your job to direct battles, but let me have the privilege of killing Hector and glorifying my name.'

Alongside Diomedes, the gigantic figure of Ajax rose up, and his thundering voice sounded like Zeus: 'I will settle

matters with Hector. Leave it to me, because I am really his equal, both in size and in courage!' Eventually, there were nine Greeks arguing that they were the best to fight Hector.

'That is how I like to see you behave; at last you have shown yourselves as valiant heroes!' cried Nestor elatedly at the Greeks. 'Now, of course, we have to choose one of you to fight Hector. I am by far the oldest of you, so perhaps I might choose, or maybe Menelaus or Agamemnon as Commander-in-Chief. However, the best thing to do is to pull a name out of a container. My helmet will do.'

'Yes, yes, let chance decide,' they all agreed and excitedly put their names into the helmet. Ajax was overjoyed when his name was drawn.

Drawing himself up to his height and in a voice like thunder, he called out, 'Now my time has come, Hector, and you will see that there are still some brave men in the Greek army. Perhaps you thought that only Achilles had enough courage and strength to face you. Not so!

Although he has left the battle, there are still enough brave men among us. Get ready quickly, Hector! Look, I am already putting on my armour.'

The Trojan hero was not affected by those words. He straightened his shoulders, puffed out his chest, and gave a curt reply: 'Ajax, do not try to scare me. I know how to wield my spear and sword, as I have proved in many battles. I could attack you now, but I do not want to cheat. I will wait until you are ready. Then I will charge at you with my spear.'

The two duellists were soon facing each other. Hector was the first to attack with his spear. It hit Ajax's shield, tore through six layers of leather, but was caught in the seventh and remained stuck. Soon Ajax launched his spear, it pierced his opponent's shield and tore Hector's tunic. However, he managed to avoid being hit. They both grabbed their spears again, pulled them out and fell on each other like two baited lions. Hector hit Ajax's shield again, but even then, it did not penetrate all the layers of leather. Ajax, sensing his chance, went into attack, but Hector escaped with only a minor scratch. He drew back, bent down, picked up a huge piece of rock and flung it at Ajax. Ajax caught it on his shield, but the blow was too fierce. He staggered, dropped the shield but still managed to pick up the nearest piece of rock. It was as big as a millstone and he hurled it at Hector. Hector fell back and it was as much as he could do to get up and grab his sword.

The glittering blades clanged against each other and blows rained on armour and helmets. First one seemed to be winning and then the other. The duel continued for many hours and still there was no clear winner.

The sun was beginning to set, and there was sweat running down Hector's and Ajax's cheeks, brows and forearms. They were becoming extremely tired and both were nearly out of breath.

When Apollo and Pallas Athene realized that the two men were equal, they sent two heralds to the battlefield. They stood between the fighters and one of

them called, 'Stop fighting! Zeus realizes that Hector is just as powerful as Ajax. But night is falling now, so you might break off the fight. You will be able to resolve the fight tomorrow.'

'I will gladly obey Zeus's instructions,' replied Ajax, 'if Hector calls off the fight. It was he who challenged the Greek leaders to a duel.'

'I did, indeed, and I am glad that you were chosen. You are a brave fighter; much stronger than any other Greek. I, too, accept Zeus's instructions — now the night is falling, it is better to stop fighting for the day and return to our own men. Why don't we exchange gifts as a token of mutual respect? I want the Greeks to say, like my own men, "They fought each other tooth and nail, did not hesitate to risk their lives but when the duel finished at the gods' request, they parted in mutual respect." Ajax, here is my silver-studded sword with its ornamental scabbard.'

Ajax praised his opponent too. He gave him a magnificent belt, which was extremely

valuable. The duel was over.

The heroes shook hands and parted. Hector returned to his father's palace, while Ajax went back to the ranks of Greek men.

In Troy Priam's advisers and leaders and the leaders of his allies met to discuss what to do the next day.

'We will send out another message to the Greeks and offer them peace,' suggested Antenor. 'After all, it was Pandarus's arrow that spoiled the last peace effort. We should return Helen and all her treasures. I think this is the best solution for the welfare of Troy.'

Paris listened to Antenor with disbelief. He rounded on him when he had finished speaking:

'What you are saying is very strange, Antenor. I find it very suspicious. Or have the gods confused you? Anyway, I will not hand over my wife, Helen, come what may. If the Greeks are after the gold and jewels that she brought with her, let them take them, for all I care. I may even add some, if that will make them go away. But that is the only thing I am willing to do.'

What decision should Priam make? He would have been glad for the war against the Greeks to come to an end and, above all, he wanted Troy to be at peace. In the end, though, he accepted Paris's suggestion.

'Early in the morning, Idaius will go to Agamemnon and

negotiate a truce for the coming day,' he decided. 'He will offer them Helen's gold and jewels and security over and above that, of course, on the understanding that Helen is staying with us. After all, she went away with Paris of her own free will. We will wait and see what answer Menelaus and Agamemnon will give.'

'I think I know what answer the Greeks will give,' said Antenor. 'They will accept the truce, but will reject the gold and jewels without Helen. The war and the siege of our city will go on!'

And things happened just as he had predicted.

The day of truce passed. On both sides, funeral fires burned and both sides surrendered their dead to the flames. Afterwards, the Greeks' camp seemed particularly busy. They were building high walls in front of the camp.

At the gods' evening feast, the god Poseidon remarked on the walls to his brother, Zeus: 'Did you notice how quickly the Greeks are building the new fortifications? In only a day, they have built a protective wall and rampart out of stones and beams and dug a deep moat in front of it. They were very keen and didn't seem to have time to offer us proper sacrifices.'

Zeus knit his brow, looked down from Olympus, let out a bolt of lightning from his

hand and made the clouds
thunder so terribly that the
Greeks, who were having their
evening meal, went pale with
fear and quickly offered some
wine to Zeus.

They were either too tired
or eager to rest before the
next day of fighting because,
despite occasional claps of
thunder from Zeus, they were
all asleep before midnight.

ON THE VERGE OF DEFEAT

The following day at dawn, Zeus called all the gods to him. He looked tired, and the lines on his forehead showed that he was annoyed. 'I called for you,' he began, 'to announce my decision. Down on the earth the Trojans and the Greeks are getting ready to renew the battle. The Trojans have already swarmed out of the city gates and are setting out to attack the Greek camp. The Greeks, hidden behind the wall which they built yesterday, are evidently waiting for a good moment to attack. It is going to be a fierce battle today and I do not want any of you to interfere. That is my order — don't ignore me.' He raised his finger in warning, looked at those around him and added in a rather more conciliatory voice, 'Do what I say. Now I am going to my seat on Mount Ida.' He got into his chariot and disappeared in the clouds.

Meanwhile, a battle was already being prepared outside Troy. Hundreds of armed men were pouring out from the city fortifications; first the men with spears and men armed with axes,

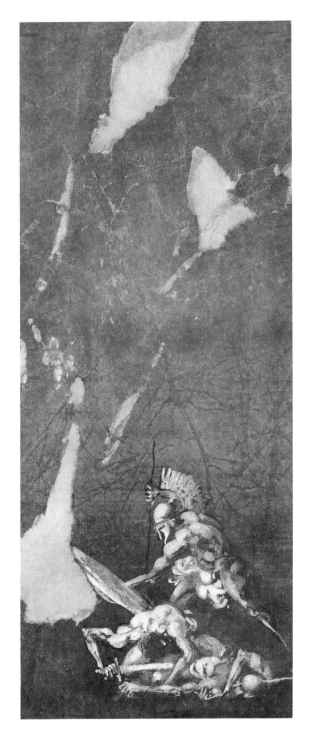

followed by more men in heavy
armour with glittering swords,
and then the charioteers
accompanied by men with bows
and arrows.

On the other side, the Greek
forces, protected by the newly
built wall, were silently waiting for
the enemy's onslaught. The
commanders were driving round
their ranks, quietly issuing orders
for the oncoming clashes. The
foot-soldiers were becoming
impatient while the horses of the
cavalrymen were beginning to
get very restless.

The fighting soon flared up;
the first ranks clashed, swords
struck helmets, arrows flew and
the roar of the battle sounded
like a thunderstorm! But it soon
became obvious that the
onslaught of the Trojan ranks led
by Hector was gaining strength.
The Greeks were forced to retreat
and their ranks were being
thrown into panic.

In the heat of battle Nestor's
horse was wounded by Paris's
arrow and when Nestor tried to
free him from the overturned
chariot, he himself was nearly
killed. Hector would certainly

have killed him if Diomedes hadn't stepped in. Diomedes's spear missed Hector but hit his charioteer, Eniopeus. Hector bent over Eniopeus and was about to be attacked by Diomedes from one side and by Nestor from the other. At that moment, a flash of lightning from Zeus appeared before Diomedes's team of horses. The dreadful reek of burning sulphur filled the air and a flame flared up from the ground.

'That is a sign of the gods!' cried Nestor in horror. 'Zeus is siding with the Trojans. We must withdraw, Diomedes! We can't go against the will of the gods!'

Diomedes was also shaken but at that moment his desire to destroy the Trojans was stronger than his fear of the gods. 'I will not run away from Hector only to become the laughing stock of our men and to let Hector boast that I ran away from him like a coward,' he replied.

'But a flash of lightning is a bad omen. What can you do against it?' Nestor retorted.

'I will have another try,' Diomedes insisted and made another attempt to attack Hector.

Diomedes rushed against Hector in his war chariot three times, but every time his team was stopped by lightning and terrific thunder.

Hector must have been greatly encouraged by these unsuccessful attempts. 'The gods are on our side!' he went on, urging the Trojans. 'We shall break through the Greeks' wall and drive them all the way to their ships. We shall set the ships on fire and the Greeks will lose all hope of winning! They will only need to see Nestor's shield or Diomedes's armour in our hands, and they will give up the struggle.'

However, on Olympus in Zeus's absence, both Hera and Pallas Athene were anxious that their protégés were being made to retreat. 'Are we really going to leave the Greeks to their fate?' said Hera, unable to restrain herself any longer. 'Shall we just watch as Hector and Paris win the struggle after all the pain they have caused us? We must do something, Pallas Athene. Zeus won't dare to oppose both of us ... and anyway, he always had a soft spot for you.'

'Yes, he has always been kind to me,' said Athene, 'especially when he sent me to rescue his son Hercules. But when Thetis fell on her knees before him and told him about sulking Achilles, he was quick to promise her that Agamemnon would not succeed,' she added irritably. 'And you are right, Hera, we should do something to encourage the Greeks. Listen, you go and get our horses ready while I go to the palace and change. I will put on my festive armour and spear and come down to the battlefield with you. I will appear to the Greeks and to Hector so that they all will see that the gods are not only on Priam's side.'

'An excellent idea,' said Hera, and before Pallas Athene returned dressed in her magnificent armour, she had

driven the chariot in front of the gates of heaven. Then she whipped up the horses, the gates thundered open and the chariot submerged in the white clouds.

The two goddesses did not go far, however. Before they were half way to the battleground, they were overtaken by Iris, the messenger of the gods. 'Stop, goddesses,' she called to them from a distance. 'Do you want to make Zeus extremely angry? He has expressly forbidden any of the Olympian family to help the armies on the plain. He saw from as far away as Mount Ida what you were about to do and he demands that you turn back. Otherwise he will lame your horses with his thunderbolt, break the chariot and hurl you both from it! Turn back the horses immediately and wait on Olympus until Zeus returns this evening.'

'I know him well. He will make all the decisions,' said Hera, offended. 'Although we are right, we can't go against Zeus. I hope we can still find a way of punishing Paris and rescuing the Greeks.'

The goddesses returned to Olympus, led the horses to the stable and sat down on their thrones. Later, towards the evening, Zeus appeared and looked as if nothing had happened.

'Why are you scowling, goddesses?' he asked. 'Whatever I do, whatever I say, you always find fault with it. Or is it because of your beloved Greeks? You must have known what my orders were. If you had disobeyed me, I would not only have struck you down with a thunderbolt, but I would have banned you from returning to Olympus!'

Hera and Pallas Athene glanced at each other. This time it was Hera who could not contain herself. 'What are you threatening us with? You act as if we had wanted to overthrow you. What you had forbidden was only that we should help the warring sides but we only wanted to advise the Greeks.'

Zeus grimaced. 'I know what I am doing, Hera,' he growled, 'and if you complain that the Greeks did badly in today's fighting, you may as well know

that they are going to do even worse tomorrow. I, too, have given a promise and I am going to keep it. Until Achilles receives a proper apology Hector will continue to be victorious. The Greeks can't win without Achilles, no one else can help them, not even you, Hera.'

Zeus called Ganymedes for his goblet of nectar and looked down through the clouds to the Trojan plain. The sun was sinking and the steadily growing darkness was making it safer for the Greeks. At last they could take a well-earned break from the fighting.

The Trojans made their camp near to the Greek fortifications and offered sacrifices to Zeus. Then they settled down to sleep. In their dreams they saw themselves storming the Greek fortifications, crossing the moat and driving Agamemnon's armies into the sea.

STAYING
APART

At that time, the Greek leaders, downcast and dispirited with the way the battle was going, gathered to hold a meeting in Agamemnon's tent. Agamemnon was pacing about the tent, stopping now and then and hardly able to hold back his tears. He spoke to his men in a choked voice:

'Friends, I am finding it difficult to speak to you. We are obviously not in Zeus's favour and I can't think what we have

done to make him suddenly deny us what he had promised before. We have been fighting Troy for such a long time and have made so many sacrifices, but yesterday's events have shown as clear as daylight that Zeus wants to preserve Troy uncaptured. Only nightfall saved us from defeat. If I am right in thinking the gods are not on our side, what sense is there in carrying on the fight? I say this with a heavy heart, but I believe we have no other option than to launch the fleet and sail home.'

There was a moment of dead silence. The Greek leaders were in despair — they sat motionless in their seats, resting their chins on the hilts of their swords and staring blankly in front of them.

Diomedes broke the oppressive silence. He rose, and took the hilt of his sword in his hand. 'I do not agree with you, Agamemnon,' he shouted. 'The gods have made you ruler of a rich and strong country, but you are not brave. Who says that we have been totally defeated? Yesterday was our enemy's day, tomorrow will be ours! We would be cowards if we fled and gave up the fighting. If you yourself want to go, take your men with you but don't wait for us. For I hope and trust that the rest will stay on. And even if all of you should leave, let me say for myself and my friend Sthenelus, we will never scuttle away from the Trojans — even if we have to fight them all alone. The gods have promised us they would help us and I still believe, in spite of everything, that I will see Priam's downfall.'

Diomedes's passionate speech roused the Greeks like the waving of a magic wand. One after the other, they lifted their heads and nodding in agreement, they gathered their weapons, jumped out of their seats and cheered.

'You have said what we all feel, Diomedes,' cried Nestor. 'Agamemnon says that Zeus doesn't favour us. But we know very well that the good fortune of war left us the moment he quarrelled with Achilles. We miss Achilles badly. Yes, Agamemnon, it is your fault, you offended him, and now it is up to you to make up for what you have done.

Apologize to Achilles, win back his favour with a gift and the Greeks will prosper again.'

King Agamemnon gave the leaders a searching look. Every expression showed that he should comply with Nestor's suggestion. The agreement, albeit a silent one, was a heavy blow to his pride. However, not even kings and leaders have a choice in such circumstances. There was nothing left to him but to give in.

'Nestor, I can't deny that Achilles's absence in the battles has cost us very dear,' he admitted reluctantly. 'If you want me to apologize to Achilles, I am willing to do so. I will even say

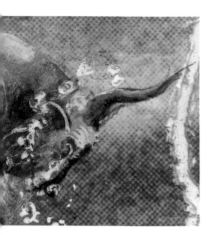

right here what I intend to offer him as a reconciliation gift: ten talents of gold, seven precious tripods, twenty beautifully polished kettles and twelve prize-winning horses. Also, seven slave girls and I will even add Briseïs into the bargain. In addition, on his return I will offer him one of my three daughters to become his wife. I am willing to do all this although I am his senior and a greater king. Let him know that above all else, I am concerned about our common cause! I hope he will stop sulking then and will rejoin our ranks. I am not going to look for him. We ought to send out a delegation to see him. You, Nestor, being the oldest, should nominate leaders to represent us. As you know, we have no time to lose!'

'Thank you for making such a wise decision,' said Nestor and asked the leaders whom they would like to propose. He himself named Phoenix first, because of his common sense and mainly because he had known Achilles from his young days and was his teacher for a time. Then someone mentioned Odysseus's

name and he was agreed. Ajax, who had given such a good account of himself in his duel with Hector, was chosen as the third, and two heralds, Odias and Eurybates, completed the number of the negotiators.

They set off at once and found Achilles outside his tent. He was sitting with his friend Patroclus, singing to the accompaniment of a lyre about the glory of war victories. When he saw the envoys, he sprang to his feet. He put down the instrument and smiled at them as though he had been expecting them for a long time:

'What distinguished visitors! Welcome, Phoenix, Ajax, Odysseus, I am always pleased to see you although I am at odds with Agamemnon. Well, come into my tent and we'll sit down at the table. My friend Patroclus will get us some food and wine. What about a saddle of mutton and a good joint of pork?' They ate their meal in silence and Achilles watched as his guests kept glancing at each other. Ajax was urging Phoenix to speak and vice versa, until, at last, Odysseus filled Achilles's cup, poured some wine for himself and the others and rose to drink a toast:

'Your health, King Achilles, and thank you for your hospitality on behalf of us all. I can see that you want to know the real reason why we are here. Let me tell you, Achilles, that our position is desperate. The Trojans have fought their way almost to the fortification which protects both our camp and our ships. They are sure to start a new assault designed to set fire to our ships and cut off our way home. Zeus is obviously on their side; he has saved Hector no less than three times! Achilles, we believe that the only thing that can save us

is your presence on the battlefield. I beg you, on Agamemnon's behalf, to forget the insults that have rightfully offended you. Stop being angry, bring your shield and your huge spear and stand alongside us. Agamemnon not only acknowledges his guilt, but he wants to make amends to you and he intends to send you rich gifts. Ten talents of gold! Seven precious tripods! Twenty polished kettles! And fine horses! And Brises! And his daughter as a bride with a rich dowry!' Odysseus exclaimed, watching Achilles's face closely for a reaction.

Achilles stared blankly into his cup and when Odysseus had finished, he drank some wine and threw an icy look at Odysseus. His words came out like a roaring fire and a raging wind:

'Have you finished, Odysseus? Well, then listen to what I have to tell you. There are no other Greeks whom I am more delighted to see than yourselves, and I am not just being polite. But just as you have always been kind to me, Agamemnon has always hated me. You are a fine speaker, Odysseus, famous for it, but words are one thing and action is another. Agamemnon gives promises, Agamemnon offers rich gifts. He has done this many times during the ten years of war against Troy! I have conquered twelve cities and I have always left the greatest part of the prize to him, although he used to do nothing while I was fighting hard battles, often against heavy odds. And what did I get? No even a word of thanks. And he crowned it all by taking Briseïs from me. You might say, "So what? She is only a slave girl." But I really loved her, Odysseus, and no gifts can make up for Agamemnon's vile action. Even if he offered me twenty times as many. And I am sure to find another father-in-law take it from me.'

'You haven't achieved much under his command! When I fought alongside the Greeks, Hector never dared to come any further than the Scaean Gate or, at most, to the oak tree. It was enough for me to appear and

Hector would draw back at once. But that is how it used to be. Now mark my words, tomorrow morning I will offer a sacrifice to Zeus, tell my men to embark and in three days, I will be at home again. Why shouldn't I? My mother Thetis always used to tell me that in fighting against Troy my life was in jeopardy, although I might win undying fame. I want to return safe and sound to my own country and after a long life, end my days in peace. And as for you, Odysseus, Ajax, Phoenix, I believe you ought to do the same. What else is left for you when Zeus evidently does not want Troy to be destroyed? After all, you, Phoenix, can stay right here and come with me. I should be happy for you to travel with me, if only because of the happy times we had together, when we were young.'

'It is exactly because of such fond memories that I beg you, Achilles, to reconsider your decision,' said Phoenix, finding it very hard to utter the words. 'I often remember the time when you were a little boy and King Peleus, your father, would ask me to look after you. We would spend whole days together; I would think up boys' games for you, tell you about your ancestors' triumphs and courage. The gods have not blessed me with a son of my own, so I just thought of you as my own and I was proud of everything you did. I cannot see why you hardened your heart so much and refuse to reconcile yourself with Agamemnon. He is begging you, Achilles. Have some pity for him. Do you really think that the Greeks, who are part of your own family, will not suffer just as badly without your help? If Hector conquers the wall and seizes the ships, he will not take pity on anybody. Would you just stand by and watch him do it?'

'Oh, my dear Phoenix,' sighed Achilles, shaking his head. 'What good times we used to have when I was toddling around your legs, or sitting on your lap! Listen, why not stay with me at least overnight; there are still so many things to talk about ...'

'But what about us, Achilles?' said Ajax raising his voice. 'Will you just send us back empty-

handed? What message can we give to the council of war? That you are a callous fellow who has no equal? That you are too proud to accept the offer of seven more slave girls for the sake of a single slave girl. How I used to respect you, Achilles!'

'Yes, for the sake of a single slave girl, Ajax,' Achilles confirmed, wiping his forehead with the back of his hand. 'My blood boils when I think of the wretched way Agamemnon treated me. But enough of that. Here is the message you are to give. You shall fight tomorrow's battle on your own, as you outnumber the Trojans. I will intervene on only one occasion: if Hector fights his way as far as the ships and threatens to set them alight and then looks for me. This is my final decision. There is nothing more to be said.'

He bowed to the envoys and waited for them to leave his tent. Four of them went; only Phoenix stayed behind, no doubt hoping that being alone with him, he would finally succeed in softening Achilles's heart.

Achilles was silent for a while. Then he reached for his cup, drank some wine and shrugged his shoulders. 'Patroclus,' he said turning to his friend, 'please tell the maids to prepare a bed for Phoenix. Fresh bedclothes and a thick blanket... let him have a good rest with us.'

He smiled at his former teacher and once again put his arms around his shoulders. 'Let us go, Phoenix,' he said.

THE NIGHT OF THE SPIES

The failure to negotiate with Achilles, which Odysseus described with great eloquence, as usual, took the entire council of war by surprise. To be honest, the Greek leaders had never anticipated such a blunt rejection. They found it hard to believe that Achilles was still so angry and that he was refusing to help them. They were gradually losing their self-confidence.

'We all made a mistake, King Agamemnon, when we tried to persuade you to give reconciliation gifts to Achilles,' burst out Diomedes. 'We know that there is no one prouder than Thetis's son. To beg him for help nourishes his pride even more. However, moaning won't get us anywhere. Let us forget Achilles and think of the best ways of preparing for the fight in a few hours' time.'

'I agree, Diomedes,' added Nestor, King of Pylos. 'But if we want to be well prepared, we must know what the enemy intends to do and how he is using his forces.'

'One of us should set out tonight on a spying expedition,' said Menelaus in an excited voice, and straightaway Diomedes shouted out, 'I will go.'

'And I will join you. Two can do more than just one — and I think that I of all people ...' said Menelaus offering himself, but Agamemnon cut him short. 'No, no, here is Ajax and Nestor, and I believe Idomeneus as well! And also Odysseus. Let Diomedes choose whom he wants to go with him. That should be the fairest way!'

He was afraid of letting his brother Menelaus go on such a perilous expedition, and he hoped that Diomedes would choose someone else.

'Let Odysseus come with me!' Diomedes decided, fulfilling Agamemnon's secret wish. 'He is a fighter like me and apart from that, he is Pallas Athene's favourite. She may help him on this expedition. As for being clever, he has the quickest brain I know.'

'You don't have to sing my praises, Diomedes,' laughed Odysseus highly flattered. 'I do not suppose I deserve them. But I will join you. We must do what

we can while it is dark. The night will not last that long. Let us go now.'

And so they went.

The leaders saw to it that the two dare-devils should have the best weapons. Thrasymedes gave Diomedes a two-edged sword, a shield and a helmet in the shape of an ox-hide cask; Meriones, Nestor's other son, gave Odysseus a bow, a quiver and a leather helmet for his head.

Under the cover of the night, they entered the plain where the Trojans and their allies had chosen to rest. As they picked their way through the debris of the last battle, they could hear the call of a heron.

'That is the voice of Pallas Athene!' said Odysseus in a whisper. 'She has promised us her help. Diomedes, that is a good sign.'

They had gone only a few steps when Odysseus suddenly stopped and pointed at something in front of him. A rapidly moving shadow was outlined against the dull sky. It was a curious figure, wearing the skin of a grey wolf, a ferret skin on his head, with an immense curved bow around his shoulders and a javelin in his right hand. He seemed to be heading for the Greek camp.

'A spy?' whispered Odysseus.

'Or a robber of the corpses?' muttered Diomedes through his teeth.

'We shall see. For now, we'll hide behind that pile of stones over there. When he comes near, we shall catch him!'

They flattened themselves on the ground, holding their breath, and watched the man who was staggering through the dark in a careless, or rather thoughtless, way. He went on, as if no harm could come to him, as if he had no enemy on earth. As he passed Odysseus and Diomedes, they

jumped up together and Diomedes flung his javelin at him. It flew over the man, stuck in the ground and started quivering.

The Trojan stopped and began to shake all over. Before he knew what had happened, the two Greek men were holding him firmly by the arms and wrists.

'Who are you? What is your name? Where are you off to?' Odysseus thundered at him.

'Dolon, my name is Dolon,' blurted the captive, turning even paler. His teeth started chattering with fear. 'Please, don't kill me. I will give you a ransom. I have enough gold and my father will give you whatever you want in return for me. He has five daughters and I am his only son!'

'So your name is Dolon. And what were you doing here? Were you robbing the dead? Or are you prowling as a spy to find out what is going on in our camp? Who put the idea into your head?' asked Diomedes pressing him hard below the throat and shaking him.

'It was Hector!' blurted out the captured Trojan. 'He promised me Achilles's horses and his war chariot if I obtained reliable information.'

'What did he want to know? Talk, you scoundrel!'

'How many sentries were posted at the Greek ships and where they were situated so that they might be carefully avoided.'

'It looks as if your Hector promised you more than you could manage. Achilles's horses! They obey only their master and would kick a mere man like you to death. And riding his chariot might at best cost you your life!' said Odysseus. Bending towards Dolon's face he hissed into his ear, 'And where is Hector now? Is he sleeping soundly in his tent or is he conferring with the Trojans and preparing for tomorrow's attack?'

'He is consulting with the leaders. They are being guarded by Trojan sentries and body-guards.'

'And what about the allies who have come to help Priam?'

'They are resting, gathering their strength. The attack is being prepared for tomorrow. After dawn, the troops are to fight their way through to the ships.'

'Are there many of them? Whereabouts are they? We want to know exactly.'

'The Carians and the Paeonian formations of archers are lying over there by the sea. And there are also many Pelasgians. On the plain near Thymbre are the camps of the Mysians and Lycians and the Maconian charioteers. The last to come were the Thracians; they did not even position any guards.'

'Who is their commander?'

'King Rhesos — he has the most beautiful horses I have ever seen. They are whiter than snow and run like the wind. And his armour is a fantastic sight…'

'Stop! You have told us enough as it is!' interrupted Diomedes. 'If we asked you more

questions, you would only make up stories. It is time to have done with it.'

'Will you set me free?' begged Dolon. 'Everything I have told you is true. Or tie me up and keep me hostage until you return. You will find out that I haven't lied to you and then you will surely set me free.'

'So that you can betray us or spy again? Forget it, Dolon, we cannot spare you; we must think of our own safety. You must be killed,' mumbled Diomedes bleakly, and his hand moved to grab his heavy sword.

Dolon raised his arms as if he were about to plead for mercy. But at that moment, Diomedes's sword whizzed through the air and struck him. Dolon was dead.

Odysseus pulled the spear and the bow from under Dolon's body, and hid them underneath a nearby tamarisk bush. Then he and Diomedes carried on. Time was passing quickly and though they had found out so much about Hector's intentions and where his forces were to be found, they desperately wanted to return with a personal prize as well. As the Thracians did not have any guards, it would surely be possible to steal Rhesos's rare white horses.

They went quickly through the dark and before long, they reached the Thracian camp. There was no guard protecting the sleeping warriors, nor their weapons which had just been thrown down outside the tents. The two beautiful white horses were standing nearby.

The two men glanced at each other. 'Dolon didn't lie,' whispered Odysseus and nodded in the direction of the horses. 'I will unharness them from the carriage, but it will take some time. You keep watch.

If necessary, you will have to kill anyone who gets in our way. No one must be allowed to betray us!'

In the darkness of the night, Odysseus got to work. He began to unfasten the animals from their harnesses, gently stroking their mauls and noses. Suddenly, Diomedes, as if he had lost his mind, drew his sword and began killing the sleeping men in a fit of fury, mingled with fear and hate.

He killed twelve Thracian leaders. The thirteenth victim was King Rhesos himself, who uttered such a load groan that it woke up his counsellor who was sleeping nearby. The counsellor raised the alarm, the sleeping men jumped to their feet and shouted, 'Arm yourselves, arm yourselves.' The Thracians were blindly running to and fro, not knowing which way to turn, and without realizing what was really going on.

They were dumbfounded when they saw the dead bodies of their comrades. After they had recovered from the shock, it was too late to chase the criminals. Odysseus and Diomedes, riding the two stolen horses, had covered a great distance.

The stamping of their hoofs was already waking the commanders at the Greek ships and the two heroes were no longer looking into the horrified eyes of the Thracians but into the triumphant faces of their comrades, who welcomed them warmly. They came running towards them from all sides and bombarded them with questions. Everyone wanted to hear what had happened on their night expedition.

'Did you get on well? Do you know what Hector intends to do? And how did you get hold of those magnificent horses? Have you any other prizes?'

'Be patient, we'll tell you everything about it. But let us rest first. We are exhausted but a swim in the sea will revive us.'

The enthusiastic Greeks accompanied Diomedes and Odysseus to the beach, where the heroes ran into the water to wash the sweat and dust from their bodies. Then they had a massage to refresh their arms and legs and finally rubbed themselves with oil until they glistened like bronze.

Meanwhile, outside the tents, Nestor, Menelaus and Agamemnon had a dinner made ready for them. When the members of the war council were seated, Nestor asked Odysseus to enlighten them. Odysseus and Diomedes took their goblets, gave thanks to Pallas Athene and set aside some meat for her.

'And now that we have thanked the goddess, I will give you an account of our expedition,' Odysseus said.

The Achaeans were literally hanging on his lips.

THE DAWN BATTLE

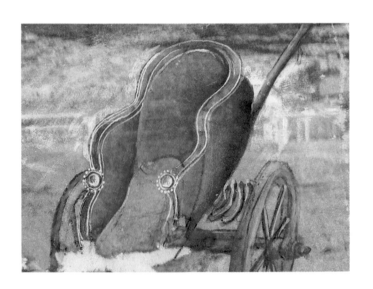

THE DAWN BATTLE

The battle broke out with the coming of the new day, shortly after dawn. The Trojans, with Hector at their head, were lined up on the hill in the middle of the plain. In his splendid armour and with his shield glittering in the sun's rays, he rushed from one rank to another, urging his men to pluck up courage and promising victory. He was accompanied by the hero Aeneas as well as other warriors. They were all convinced that it was Zeus's will that this day would see the Greeks defeated.

However, the Greeks, too, had been ready for battle since the early morning. The Commander-in-Chief, Agamemnon, was wearing magnificent armour. Since Odysseus and Diomedes

returned from their successful expedition, he seemed to have recovered his old self-confidence. He was longing to meet the enemy again.

A light morning breeze was blowing over Troy. Suddenly the peaceful atmosphere of the morning was pierced by a mighty roar rising above the plain, high into the clouds.

The outposts clashed, the battle flared, and in the brief encounter, the Greeks were winning. Before long, they were within view of the Scaean Gate, and the Trojans began to waver.

Hector was about to mount a counter-attack to stem the Greek advance but he recalled what Iris had revealed to him when the battle began: 'Hector, do not intervene with your weapon while Agamemnon is raging on the battlefield. Your time will come only when the King of Mycenae is wounded. Then you will stop the Greeks, and the road to their ships behind the fortification will be open to you.'

He went over Iris's words again but he was greatly tempted to meet Agamemnon face to face in the battle.

Agamemnon was on the wet ground behind the sacred oak tree fighting the young Iphidamus who had sailed to help the Trojans with twelve ships from distant Thracia. Agamemnon had lost his spear in the fierce encounter, but he still had enough strength and keen perception to draw his sword in time and hit Iphidamus. As he was bending over his defeated enemy, Coon, Iphidamus's brother, suddenly emerged and thrust his spear against Agamemnon. The Greek leader felt a sharp pain above his elbow, but he managed to throw off Coon and jumped into his chariot. He ordered his charioteer to rush him to the ships.

'Agamemnon is leaving! Faithful Trojans and you, our allies, Dardanians, Lycians, Mysians and the rest of you, close your ranks! Our time has come at last! By the evening we shall have taken the fortification and reached their ships.'

Hector's order was soon heard by every man. Those running

away stopped, regrouped and didn't give another inch of the ground to the Greeks. They began to surround the wedge which the enemy was using to break through to the Scaean Gate.

Diomedes realized the danger and to avert disaster, stepped out against Hector, attacking him with his spear. He aimed at his head, but Hector's helmet softened the blow. Hector staggered, sank to his knees and fainted for a moment.

'You scoundrel! Phoebus Apollo has saved you again!' yelled Diomedes in fury. 'But we shall get you in the end!' With his sword drawn and uttering threatening cries, he ran towards Hector, who was rising slowly, groping about with his hands. Diomedes was just about to kill Hector when he felt a sharp,

burning pain in his right foot. An arrow shot by Paris had stuck in his foot.

'You have been hit,' he shouted triumphantly. 'If I had hit you somewhere else, Troy could have been rid of you for ever, you murderer of our heroes!'

'Paris!' moaned Diomedes in reply. 'This is the first time you have appeared on the battleground and even now you are only firing from a safe distance. You have just scratched the sole of my foot and you are boasting about it. I will give you what for. Just wait till I pull the arrow out of my foot!'

'No, no, Machaon must treat you. Run, I will cover you,' cried Odysseus. He had rushed to help his fellow fighter who was mopping the blood out of the wound with a tuft of grass. Diomedes was wincing with pain and as he tugged at the arrow in his foot, his eyes filled with tears.

'Thank you, Odysseus,' he shouted and jumped into the chariot.

At that moment, Odysseus was attacked by Socos, Priam's wealthy grandson. 'Now it is your turn to die!' he roared and flung his spear until it stuck in Odysseus's shield. The point pierced it and ripped Odysseus's skin. He recovered immediately and although he was covered in blood, he felt sure the wound was not fatal.

'You are wrong, Socos! It is not me but you who is destined to die today,' he shouted and struck Socos a well-aimed, deadly blow between the shoulder blades. Socos groaned and collapsed.

Odysseus stood over the dead Trojan and exhausted by the struggle, was panting for breath. He, too, staggered and heard cries coming from far away: 'Odysseus is wounded. Save the King of Ithaca!'

The spearmen, who noticed that Odysseus was bleeding, got together, and led by Ajax, rushed against the Trojans with a deafening roar. Ajax, with his shield held high, was fighting his way towards Odysseus and as he was approaching him, gave a triumphant war-cry with every blow of his sword: 'Odysseus, they are on the run, they are on the run!'

On the banks of the Scamander river, the Trojans were fighting with more success. Hector, in his war chariot, led the battle wisely. The Dardanians and Mysians slowly but surely began to push back the Cretans as well as Nestor's men. The archers, led by Paris, were gaining ground.

The fierceness of the fighting increased and the number of victims rose quickly. The plain was littered with dead bodies but in their fury the warriors attacked each other again and again, strode over the dead bodies, discarded shields and broken spears and staggered over the wheels of the overturned chariots. Inevitably they began to get weaker. Even Ajax was finding it hard to swing his sword, and he began to retreat.

Achilles was watching the changing fortunes of war from his ship. He witnessed the early successes of the Greeks and their later retreat, which was slowly turning into a flight. Among the fleeing warriors, he also noticed Nestor; he was

taking a wounded man to safety in his war chariot.

'Patroclus,' Achilles called to his old friend who was looking concerned about the outcome of the battle, 'did you notice Nestor's chariot? He had a wounded man there. I thought I recognized Machaon, but they dashed past so quickly that I did not see his face. Go to Nestor and find out if I was right.'

'Yes, of course, Achilles,' Patroclus nodded. He started running but then he stopped suddenly, undecided. He sighed.

'Do you fear that this day is not going to work out well for the Greeks?' he said. 'Any time now, they will come and beg me to join the fight on their side,' answered Achilles.

'And what will you say, Achilles?'

'We shall see. Now go and see Nestor first. I am sorry if Machaon is injured for he is surely our best doctor. Hurry, Patroclus, go at once!'

Achilles's friend found both the leaders resting. When Nestor saw Patroclus, he beckoned him in and asked him to sit down. 'Will you have a drink with us before you tell us why you have come?' asked Nestor.

Patroclus shook his head. 'I have come only to ask you about something, your majesty,' he said. 'But now I don't need to. Achilles was anxious to learn whom you had brought wounded from the battle.'

'I can hardly believe my ears,' replied Nestor. 'Is Achilles sometimes sorry for the fate of Greek fighters? Does he know how many have already died and how many have been wounded? It seems to me that when he wants to see the battleground he does, and when he does not, he sends a messenger. So, tell him that not only has Machaon been shot with an arrow but that Agamemnon, too, has been wounded. Odysseus has been pierced by Socos's spear, and Eurypylus has had an arrow in his thigh. But the proud Achilles is not really worried about such things — he prefers to wait until our ships go up in flames.'

Patroclus listened to the King of Pylos with his head lowered. 'I see what you mean, Nestor.

But you know how quick-tempered and stubborn Achilles is. He will not be moved easily. And once he has decided that he will not join the fight before the Greek ships are threatened by the Trojans … Nevertheless, if I can be of any help.'

'I know better than anyone how hot-tempered the King of the Myrmidons is,' said Nestor. 'But remind him what his father tried to impress upon me before we sailed for Troy: "Achilles is good, but he also needs a good adviser and as you are older and more level-headed, you ought to be able to advise and help him whenever necessary." These are the exact words of Peleus and you should repeat them to Achilles. If he hears them from his closest friend, they may coax him into action. And give him my other message as well. If he wants to stick to his decision and not fight — and he may well be doing that to please his mother — there is at least one thing he can do for the Greeks. He can lend you his magnificent armour, his shield and sword. If you put on his armour and appear on the

battlefield, the Trojans would be convinced that Achilles had come back. They would stop fighting at least for a time, and this would give us a much-needed rest. Go and tell him.'

'I will, Nestor. I will try to persuade Achilles. And you pray to the Olympian gods to accept what you have suggested. As far as I am concerned, I am more than ready to do it.'

He turned, ran out of the hut and hurried towards Achilles's ships.

By Odysseus's ship, the place where they held their assemblies and their legal sessions, he ran into Eurypylus limping back from the battle. Sweat was pouring down his forehead, blood ran from his wound in the thigh and he had to stop after every third or fourth step. His face reflected all the wretchedness and cruelty of battle.

'Come, I will help you!' cried Patroclus in distress. 'I cannot leave you to fend for yourself in such a state.'

He took Eurypylus under the arms and supporting him gently, led him into the tent. He called the servants to spread a cowhide and laid him upon it. Then he carefully removed the arrow, washed off the blood with warm water and spread soothing powder on the wound.

'I feel better now,' whispered Eurypylus, gratefully squeezing Patroclus's arm. 'But what will happen next? Can we resist the Trojans successfully? Can we succeed in standing up to Hector?'

THE STORMING OF THE WALL

The moment Hector found out that King Agamemnon had left the battlefield, he ordered a counterattack to be launched. The Trojans' assault was like a gale that smashes and carries along everything that stands in its way.

Thinking that victory was within reach, Hector pursued the Greeks with the ferocity of a lion. He was one of the first to fight their way to the deep trench dug outside the wooden fortress which protected the Greek fleet and their camp.

Here, suddenly, the first wave of war chariots and riders came to a halt. The horses neighed and dug their hooves into the ground. They were terrified by the steep walls on either side of the trench and by the pointed stakes.

'Hector, it would be madness to drive the horses through here,' shouted Polydamas, Hector's

adviser, jumping from his chariot. 'Even if we could get down, how can we clamber up to the walls? But I have an idea. We will leave the chariots until we get back and we will storm the wall fortification on foot.'

'You are right, Polydamas. The gods must be on our side if they gave you such an idea,' said Hector brightening up. He decided at once. 'We will attack in five waves and will go forward close to one another, in our ranks and protected by shields. Who shall I put in the lead? My charioteer, Kebriones, and you, Polydamas, will come with me. The second detachment will be led by Paris and Agenor. Our allies from Arisbe will be led by Asius and the fourth will be headed by Aeneas and the two sons of Antenor, Acamas and Archelochus. The fifth company will be formed by our allies from Lycia under the leadership of Sarpedon, together with his cousin Glaucus.'

But before the Trojans managed to rally according to Hector's orders, the crack of a whip was heard, and Asius, together with his men, rushed forward to carry out an independent attack at the left flank. He raced his team of horses to the high oak causeway left open for the last fleeing Greeks and guarded by two strong Thessalian champions. They stood still in front of the high gate and Asius believed that his soldiers would cope with them easily. But when they started running against them, they were met with blows of clubs and a shower of rocks. The boulders, which were hurled from the gate towers, pierced helmets and broke shields and shin guards. The attack had lost its momentum even before it had started properly.

'Attack! Attack!' shouted Hector on the other side of the line, wielding his sword. He rushed forward to the trench.

Paris, Agenor, Helenus, Sarpedon and the other commanders followed him. The Greeks were hurling stones, firing arrows and casting their javelins and spears. But before long it would be over and the proud ships with their red prows would be destroyed.

The Trojans were already imagining their triumph, when suddenly a huge eagle appeared above their heads. It circled round, dropped slowly down and was seen to be carrying a writhing snake in its claws. The huge snake was wriggling and raising itself against the eagle's breast every now and then. Suddenly the astonished Trojans saw it dart and dig its poisonous fangs into the bird's chest. The eagle uttered a cry of pain and disappeared into the clouds. The snake dropped to the earth in the middle of the Trojan ranks and lay motionless. The Trojans stared at it and felt very uneasy about what they had seen.

'Stop the attack!' shouted Polydamas, terrified. 'The gods obviously do not want us to get into the Greeks' camp. They are giving us a sign — the eagle flew from the left to the right and did not carry his prey to his nest. We wouldn't do any better. Let's stop

the battle for the time being.'

But this time Hector opposed him: 'Your advice is worthless, Polydamas! Just because a bird flew past us, does that mean that we should let the Greeks have a break? Just when they are fleeing and are confused? I do not take any notice of the flight of birds. The only order I want to obey is to fight to the last breath for the city of my birth. Zeus is on our side — look how a gale is driving dust and sand towards the Greek camp from Mount Ida. A sandstorm like that is bound to make that defence much more difficult. We can go forward in the clouds of dust right up to the walls, and they won't see us. We must fight on. Onward!'

Hector's words reassured the Trojans and they readily accepted the challenge. Sarpedon, leader of the Lycians, backed by his cousin Glaucus, charged against the tower which was defended by Menestheus and Ajax. 'Tear up the pillars and beams in the palisade!' he roared at his men as they clambered onto the steep wall of the trench, protecting themselves against the arrows and boulders flung by the defenders.

Crouching underneath the walls, the Trojans tried to force their way inside using axes and crowbars. Finally, Sarpedon, with his powerful spade-like hands, prized open a piece of the rampart. But his men were too tired from the previous fighting to fight their way through the opening. The Greeks quickly covered it with their shields and anything else that came to hand.

'Attack! Attack!' cried Hector tirelessly. 'Hold out, men, and break through the Greek wall!' He lifted up an enormous bolder that two well built men would find hard to carry. He held it over his head, gasping for breath, but when he spread his legs, it became much lighter to carry. Zeus himself must have given him the strength to do it. Slowly he made for the gate, stopped, swung the boulder over his head and flung it for all he was worth against the gate. The wood creaked, the gate was thrown off its hinges, the bars burst and the gates opened to let the troop pass through.

Hector picked up his two javelins, straightened the armour on his chest and stretched out his right hand. 'Go through the gates, Trojans, victory is within reach!'

Like a wild river, the Trojans and their allies rushed inside, some through the gate, others by climbing the walls, all exhilarated by the prospect of an early triumph and rich prizes. Hector was walking among them, swinging his javelins over his head and showing the dignity of a commander who knows that his dream about the enemy's crushing defeat is near at hand. At the same time, the Greek army was retreating in wild confusion.

THE REVERSAL

While the fighting was going on in Troy, Zeus was resting and amusing himself on Mount Ida. It never occurred to him that one of the gods might interfere in the fighting near the Greek camp because he had ordered all of them not to.

Zeus's brother, Poseidon, also kept a sharp look-out for what was happening on the earth. However, his attention was drawn to the plain of Troy. He had a grudge against the Trojans for having greatly insulted him once. When he saw that the Greeks had been forced to retreat, he was sorry for them. So he resolved to help them. He harnessed his horses to his royal chariot, put on his magnificent armour and whipped the horses with his golden whip. He touched the surface of the sea with his trident and the chariot drove out across the waves. The sea monsters fled from their ruler and made way for him.

Poseidon hid his sea chariot in a cavern on the island of Imbros near Troy and made his way to the Greek camp. It was a very

gloomy scene. There were warriors running to and fro, sitting with their heads in their hands by the ships; many were tending injuries or dressing their wounds. Poseidon noticed two brave men in particular. Both were called Ajax, one the King of Salamis and the other the son of the King of Locris. These two seemed to be the least shaken. He took the form of Calchas, the prophet, and spoke to them in an encouraging way:

'I hope you do not think that all is lost after one defeat in a skirmish. Hold on, for even the Trojans will get tired and run out of patience. You have enough weapons and the Greeks have never lacked courage.'

He reached out and touched the two men with his divine sceptre. At that moment, they both felt immense strength and freshness pour into their veins. They stared at the prophet with amazement and although he was speaking and acting like Calchas, they were sure that someone else was speaking to them. It must have been one of the gods, for immediately after he

had spoken, he vanished from their sight.

By then, Poseidon was facing the ranks of the Aitolians and Boeothians who, exhausted, had retreated to their ships. They had lost their weapons and they looked very weary.

'Well, you're a fine sight,' said Poseidon, who was once again in the form of Calchas. 'I thought you were waiting to defend your ships and instead you are just waiting for Hector to deal you another blow. Those Trojans! You have always boasted that they are like rabbits who will run away if you merely stamp you feet. Do they seem like panthers to you now? Don't blame Agamemnon and his quarrel with Achilles. That would make you look like cowards. Look, Ajax of Salamis is already encouraging his men to fight. Go and join them quickly so that you won't feel ashamed when you face them after they have defeated Hector's men!'

As if they had been touched by a magic wand, the men sprang up, gathered their swords and spears and tightly closed

their ranks so that their shields and helmets touched one another.

'Idomeneus!' thundered Poseidon's voice again, when he saw him carrying a wounded fighter to the ship. 'Why are you withdrawing from the fight? Your friend can look after himself. Those who leave the battle are cowards. Stand up again to the Trojans; you won't be alone. The more there are, the stronger you will be.'

Idomeneus was taken aback. Why should he have to listen to such talk when he was one of the bravest fighters? Why should anyone doubt him? He thumped his armour with his fist, lifted his right arm brandishing two spears and turned back to the battle.

Once again, the Trojans and the Greeks and their allies fought against each other and many were killed. No one spared his opponent; both sides were filled with hatred. The monstrous fury of the armies was merciless.

Among those killed was Imbrius, King Priam's son-in-law. Hector was too late to help him, but he threw a spear at his killer, Teucer, which hit Amphimachus, the grandson of Poseidon, in the chest. Poseidon loved Amphimachus very much and his death made him hate the Trojans even more. He uttered a tremendous shout as if ten

thousand men, rushing forwards the enemy, had all roared at once.

The battle raged ceaselessly. The earth shook, the number of wounded men grew and the Greeks, backed by Poseidon, began to launch a counter-attack.

Hector called for Polydamas to advise him when the unexpectedly stubborn Greek resistance would finally be broken. He asked him numerous questions: Where was Adamas and how was his brother, Helenus, standing up to the fray? Where was Imbrius? What about Othryoneus?

'Most of them have been killed, only Deiphobus and Helenus escaped with wounds. They are being treated in the city,' Polydamas replied. 'I warned you that the eagle was a bad omen for us. You would not listen to me. Although we are through to the Greek camp, victory is still far away. Most of the Trojans are interested in nothing but prizes and some are leaving the battlefield!'

'Polydamas, this is not good news. But a struggle is a struggle and I do not intend to give it up. I will take over the leadership again and stir our men — look, here comes Ajax. I will take care of him. This will encourage the Trojans and put new life into them!'

'You fool, do you think you will scare us when you walk around as if you were taking a stroll along the seashore?' growled Ajax, spitting out his words between clenched teeth. 'Are you after our ships? You might as well give up the idea. Before you reach them, we will have demolished your celebrated Troy. And you will not have a horse fast enough to take you out of here!'

Hector shook his head and lifted his eyes to the sky, just as an eagle was flying by, this time from right to left.

'You are a chatterbox, Ajax, and you do not know what you are talking about. This day will ruin you. I will kill you with this spear and send you to Hades's underground kingdom. The dogs and ravens will feed on your body. You have lost. Just one

more attack, my fearless Trojans, and Greek pride will be broken. Let's go.'

Hector's spear whizzed through the air and struck Ajax, but the harness on his chest deadened the shock and saved his life. While Hector looked around for someone to hand him a new weapon, Ajax took advantage and bent down to tear up a piece of rock. He flung it at Hector with great force. The boulder hit him near his neck and he fell to the ground.

'Hector! Hector!' The Trojan hero was joined by Polymadas, Aeneas, Agenor, Parpedon and Glaucus, all close comrades, who immediately covered their comrade with their shields. 'Let us carry him away quickly. He must be attended to. Let us hurry to the Scamander river and wash his wound there. There is blood around his mouth and his breath is wheezing. We mustn't let Priam's son be killed at the dirty hands of the Greeks.'

Thanks to the care of Polydamas and the others, Hector slowly came round on the bank of the Scamander river. However, without their commander the Trojans were lost and shaken. They no longer found strength to resist and began to retreat through the gate. The god Poseidon, who had supported the Greeks so effectively, was delighted and deeply satisfied. So was the goddess Hera on the heights of Olympus. For she, too, had followed the struggle of the Greeks, and, like Poseidon, had helped them in the fight, although none of them had any inkling of it.

ZEUS
INTERVENES

Zeus woke up from his sleep, feeling pleasantly refreshed. He rose from his golden bed, stretched himself, and looked down on the earth on the plain of Troy. What he saw instantly spoilt his good mood. He rubbed his eyes to make sure that he was not dreaming, and again looked towards the Scamander river. Was it possible? Hector was lying there with glazed eyes, his comrades were tending him, while the other Trojans were fleeing from the battlefield, pursued by the Greeks. And even Poseidon could be seen among them now and then, as if the word of Zeus was not worth a button. To make matters worse, he was helping the Greeks and had broken his promise.

Zeus angrily ran his fingers through his beard. He now knew the real situation. And he also realized why Hera had travelled all the way to Mount Ida — to distract his attention from what was happening on earth. While she was flattering him and he was enjoying her company, she had sent Poseidon to help the Greeks.

'Hera, I will not stand for this,' murmured the ruler of Olympus and clapped his hands. Hera appeared before him with an innocent smile on her face.

'Hera, this was your bright idea to knock Hector out of the fight. While you were keeping me company, Poseidon, at your instigation, was rescuing the Greeks,' Zeus thundered. 'You are annoying me, and presuming that you can get away with anything, but I am warning you! I have bound you in golden chains in the clouds between heaven and earth once before — take care or I will do it again. Admit that this was your doing!'

Zeus was raging and yelling enough to make anyone frightened. Hera's pleasant smile disappeared. She knew only too well that her husband would carry out his threats and if he felt even slightly offended, he would not hesitate to take revenge.

'How could I dare to do anything like that, my noble husband,' she said in a humble voice. 'Poseidon decided this by himself — you know he is not fond of the Trojans. Actually,

he suddenly felt sorry for the Greeks. Surely this shouldn't make you feel so bad. Ask him to come and see you and he is sure to understand your reasons for not wanting the Trojans to be defeated.'

'I expect he will understand my reasons,' said Zeus raising his brows thoughtfully. His worst rage died down when he contemplated the lovely Hera: 'This is my decision. You will go to Olympus and give a message to Iris to come to me here on Mount Ida. I also want to see the archer Apollo. Ask them to come right away – I won't have any excuses! I have important assignments for them.'

'I will go with pleasure,' said Hera, and was only too happy to get out of Zeus's sight.

Zeus was glad to see that both Iris and Apollo had come to Mount Ida as quickly as they could. They bowed politely to Zeus as they heard from Hera that they shouldn't irritate him in any way. They guessed that the divine couple had had yet another quarrel, and on such occasions, Zeus could rage at the slightest opportunity.

'Iris, you are to go and find my brother Poseidon, and tell him to come either to his palace under the sea or to Olympus. This is an order! I will not tolerate his helping the Greeks. He has already offended me. As for you, Apollo, you must look for Hector on the bank of the Scamander where he is being treated. Here is a magic shield decorated with two tassels. It will protect you and Hector from the Greeks. You must stand at the head of the Trojans and chase Agamemnon's army as far as the ships. Then I will decide what to do with the Greeks. Go now. I am tired and want to rest for a while.'

When Poseidon received Zeus's message from Iris, he shouted at her as if she were responsible for what it said:

'What does Zeus think he is doing? Who is he to tell me whom I can help and whom I can't? Zeus and Hades, the King of the Dead, are my brothers and we have more or less the same rights. He has no right to order me about like he orders his many children. Is he just trying to irritate me, or does he think I will put up with anything from him?'

Poseidon was in a rage. Iris wanted to know whether she had to relate to Zeus what Poseidon had said. Once again, Poseidon rounded upon her, saying, 'Wait. Tell him from me that this time I will give in. But only for the sake of good will. I am willing to come to an agreement, but if he wants to spare Troy, I will not recognize him as my brother. Besides, Hera and Hephaistos, to say nothing of Pallas Athene, will not agree with him.'

With these words, he threw himself into the waves, while Iris, like a soft breeze, flew up to the sky, lightly waving her heraldic staff.

Apollo had a basic task. When he arrived at the bank of the Scamander, Hector could already sit up and even make a few steps, helped by his friends. As he felt his strength slowly returning, he even tried to lift his spear. He was sure he would be well enough to resume the fight before long. They handed him his helmet and he put it on.

Apollo followed him with a smile and began to encourage

him: 'I can see you have recovered, Hector. I have brought you some good news. I am Phoebus Apollo, god of the sun and of light. The arrows on my silver bow never miss their target. Zeus has followed your struggle and he has sent me to help you chase the Greeks to their ships. Now we will go and stand at the head of your men. I will protect you with this magic shield and open the way for you with my golden sword. We will make the Greek warriors run away again.'

Hector's reappearance on the battlefield was like a bolt from the blue for the Greeks. They couldn't believe that he was still alive after having been hit by Ajax. And who was the man fighting at his side who held the magnificent flaming shield which stopped every arrow and stone flung at them? He accompanied Hector right up to the trench. He scrambled up the fortification, demolished part of it and made a passage for the Trojans so that they could move forward and attack both the gate and the ramparts at close quarters.

The Greeks' hearts sank into their boots when they saw Hector standing unhurt in the middle of the Trojans. His eyes were glowing at his opponents and no one was able to stop him as he was protected by the magic shield. However, all the Greek heroes tried their best to defeat Hector. As they did so, the voice of Ajax, son of Telamon, could be heard:

'Do your best, Greek heroes. Think of your parents, your wives and your children. Set them a good example. You can save yourselves – none of us must give way. If we die, we shall at least be praised, for there is no greater honour than losing your life for your country!'

The Greeks did what Ajax said and formed a defensive ring around their ships, but Hector could not be stopped. In an unrelenting struggle, Priam's son fought his way to one of the ships, caught a hold of its stern, jumped aboard and cut down the point of Ajax's spear. And from the ship's stern, swinging his sword, he cried victoriously, 'Trojans, Zeus has given us victory. I was right when I said that he was on our side. Hurry up with the torches, we will set fire to the ships that have brought us so much misery!'

Five or six flaming torches were thrown at the first conquered ship. The fire soon spread through the ship and before long it was completely ablaze; the ship of Protesilaus, the hero who a long time ago when the fighting had started was the first to touch the Trojan shore.

WEARING ACHILLES'S ARMOUR

While the fierce fighting was raging close to the Greeks' defensive wall, Patroclus was carefully tending the wounded Eurypylus. Now and then he could hear voices calling out, but he remained calm. As the voices grew stronger and more numerous and it seemed that the armies were quite near, Patroclus went outside the tent and was appalled. Groups of Greeks were dashing past, wounded warriors were being dragged along, riderless horses stumbled against pierced shields and broken spears. What more evidence was needed to show that the Greeks had lost the battle?

'Achilles!' the thought flashed instantly through Patroclus's mind. 'Achilles must be told of this right now.'

Leaving his servants to look after Eurypylus, he hurried to find Achilles. Soon he stood before him with tears in his eyes.

'What is the matter, Patroclus? Why are you in tears?' said Achilles by way of welcome. 'Is there bad news from home? Has anything happened to your father? Or are you sorry that the Greeks can't overcome Hector, whatever they do? Tell me.'

'Achilles, my dear friend, reports from the battlefield are very bad. The Greeks are suffering one disaster after another. Diomedes cannot fight; he was wounded by a spear. Nor can Agamemnon carry on the struggle. Eurypylus has a terrible wound in his thigh and Odysseus also suffered an injury. We barely have a commander left who is unhurt.' Patroclus went on until he nearly choked. 'Achilles, won't you take pity on us even now? We must stop the Trojans when they have driven so far behind the walls. If you want to keep out of the fighting because of some ill-omened prophecy, lend me your armour. If I appear with it on, the Trojans will stop their assault and this will let our men rest. In fact, you promised Odysseus and Ajax that you would, and I think…'

'What kind of stories are you telling me, Patroclus? That I am keeping out of the fighting because of some prophecy?' Achilles cut his friend short. 'You can't believe that. We have been friends for too long. It is only Agamemnon's insult that still smarts and hurts me.' He fell silent and waved his hand. 'All right, let bygones be bygones. But you can't expect me to go back on my word. I have said that I won't take part in the fighting until the Trojans threaten

my own fleet. And this has not yet happened. However, I will lend you my armour and let you take the ranks of the Myrmidons, but only until you drive Hector out of the camp. When you have done that, you must return! Do not lead your men to Troy — that is a job for me. We don't want Agamemnon to broadcast that he defeated Hector's ranks even without Achilles! Come on, I will help you to put on the armour. Automedon, harness Xanthus, Balius and Pedasus, and get the war chariot ready! And let the commanders sound the alarm!'

Achilles handed Patroclus his own shining armour; first, the shin greaves with silver clips, then the decorated breast plate, the bronze shield and finally the sword decorated with silver rivets. Then he chose two spears, but he did not give him the famous unbreakable ash javelin, it was so heavy that only he could handle it.

Meanwhile, the Myrmidons were forming into five ranks, headed by experienced soldiers. They had all had a rest and

Achilles's orders to join the battle were greeted with cheers. Before they set out, Achilles ran to his tent and filled a goblet with wine. As he poured drops of the wine onto the earth, he raised his eyes to the sky and spoke to Zeus.

'Ruler of Olympus, you granted my wish when you let the Greek army be so heavily defeated. Now grant me this wish as well. I am sending my friend, Patroclus, with the Myrmidons into the battle. Give them strength so that they can show how courageous they are and so that Hector will see what a great friend Achilles has.'

Then the Myrmidons, led by Patroclus, rushed at the Trojans. The first assault was unsuccessful. However, when Patroclus joined the second assault, the Trojans were thrown into turmoil. 'Look, it is Achilles dashing on his war chariot and he has brought his Myrmidons with him!' the Trojans shouted in alarm. 'Achilles must have been reconciled with Agamemnon. Look how ferociously he is fighting, killing those who attacked the Greek fleet.'

The sun was shining over the battlefield but the fighting was obscured by clouds of dust kicked up by the horses' hoofs. Men fell headlong under the wheels of their chariots. Horseriders tumbled from their startled horses and foot-soldiers staggered over dead bodies on the ground. Some were still defending themselves on their knees with whatever strength they had left, others fled and retreated from the refreshed and rested Myrmidons who were pressing them on all sides.

At their head, Patroclus, in Achilles's splendid armour, was fighting like mad. First, he drove the Trojans away from Protesilaus's vessel and had the fire put out. Then he turned his ranks against the Lycians of Hector's friend, Sarpedon. Before long, the camp was cleared and the Trojans started to turn back to the city walls.

In the middle of the terrible battle, Patroclus came across Sarpedon. Both jumped off their chariots and rushed at each other like two vultures. Patroclus was the first to charge, but his

spear missed Sarpedon and hit
his charioteer. Then Sarpedon
attacked, but his aim was not
better. Sarpedon's spear again
whizzed through the air and
missed Patroclus's shoulder by
a hair's breadth. 'Your end has
come!' cried Patroclus, who leapt
forward and stretched his arm —

Sarpedon fell to the ground.

As the Greeks were taking off the dead hero's armour, Apollo picked up Sarpedon's body and carried it off to the bank of the distant river. There, he washed away the blood and dust, anointed him with ambrosia and entrusted him to Hypnos, god of Sleep, and Thanatos, god of death.

The Greek victory was complete. The Trojan and allied ranks were beaten and seeking refuge near the city walls. The armour of the dead soldiers was taken as prizes and captured warriors were being kept to work as slaves. The Greeks were celebrating their victory on the plain outside Troy while Patroclus was driving around the ranks in his chariot. He didn't seem to be aware of the greatness of the moment. His eyes were fixed on the Scaean Gate of Troy where he could see Hector among the crowds.

'Hector,' he murmured to himself and pressed his sword firmly in his hand. 'The battle is not finished until I have run this weapon through your chest...

I will not go back before I have
killed you. I must get you, I will
sort you out.'

Achilles's warning was forgotten. Patroclus raised his right
hand and Automedon heard his
fatal order, 'Let's get Hector!'

PATROCLUS
IS KILLED

During all the downturn in the long and unrelenting battles with the Greeks, Hector kept a cool head. Even now, he was trying to direct the quick retreat of the Trojans so that they would suffer as few losses as possible. He was convinced that the Trojans needed some rest, that the most reasonable course would be to withdraw behind the city walls and to refresh themselves there

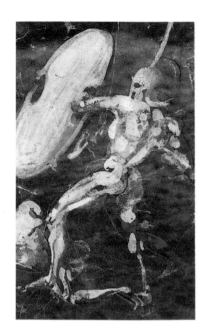

in safety. But he was stopped at the Scaean Gate by Apollo.

'Are you leaving the battlefield?' the god asked, pretending to be surprised. 'You are not showing much confidence in Zeus, who has promised you success. Who do you think you are facing? Achilles? You are only fighting his armour. Perhaps, in the heat of the battle you did not have time to notice, but take it from me, you have not fought with Achilles but with Patroclus! You surely haven't run away from him; although he is brave, he is not destined to destroy Troy.'

Hector felt breathless and his heart started to drum. 'So, it was Patroclus who changed the fortune of the battle,' he said, grinding his teeth. 'Was it his disguise that made our army run?'

'Yes, Hector. But with my help you can reverse everything,' answered Apollo. Patroclus's war chariot was dashing towards them and, even at that distance, Hector could see a triumphant look at his face.

'Cebriones!' he shouted.

'Prepare the horses! We will meet him. And you, Trojans, follow me!'

Hector leapt from his chariot and, with his spear in one hand and his sword in the other, stepped in front of Patroclus. Patroclus was walking slowly towards Hector. He clutched his spear in his left hand and in his right hand he held a sparkling stone which he had picked up on the way. The two men stopped and stared with hatred at each other. Then suddenly Patroclus threw the sparkling stone, which whizzed past Hector's shoulder but fatally wounded Cebriones.

Hector was seized by a desire to avenge Cebriones's death and he charged forward with the other Trojans. The ranks clashed and the leaders were fighting in the middle of a wild crush. No one wanted to surrender. Both the Greeks and the Trojans were roaring and howling and both sides were trying to grab Cebriones's body.

The second day of the battle was drawing to its close. Three times a crowd of the Trojans surrounded Patroclus and each time he stood his ground and

killed nine attackers. But when the Trojans attacked for the fourth time, a strange mist suddenly appeared behind his back. Achilles's dearest friend, as if suspecting something odd, made a slight turn. All at once, as the mist drew close to him, he felt a heavy blow on his back. Apollo's hand then emerged from the cloud and knocked the helmet from his head. Patroclus was badly shaken. Then one of the Trojans knocked the spear out of his hand. The hero staggered and rounded on the attacker. As he did so his shield slipped out of its strap on his forearm and fell to the ground. He bent to pick it up and the armour covering his chest came loose and exposed his body.

'That is not Achilles! That is not the King of the Myrmidons!' cried a sharp squeaky voice from the throng of the Trojans. It belonged to a very young fighter called Euphorbus. Two or three times he bleated this out before he plucked up courage and stuck his spear into Patroclus's back.

'I have killed Patroclus!' he yelled. However, as if terrified by

the thought that Patroclus might have enough strength to kill him, too, he hid his face in his hands and disappeared into the throng of the horrified Trojans.

Patroclus, his face distorted with pain, was trying to pull the spear out of his back. He felt his strength oozing away rapidly, but his desire to live gave him supernatural strength. He staggered, tugging at the spear with one hand and stretching the other before him like a blind man looking for something to hold on to. Then he took a step and another – and with that his fate was sealed. Hector, seeing that Patroclus was trying to escape, made his way to him and thrust a spear into his sides.

Patroclus fell to the ground with a thud. Hector stood over him and cried, 'Patroclus, did you think that you would win Troy and that everybody would run away from you if you appeared in Achilles's armour? You forgot that you still had to deal with Hector who never runs away from battle or from anybody! Now you are dying and the armour which your friend helped you to put on will be mine.'

For the last time, Patroclus rallied his strength and, overcoming the pain, he leaned on his elbow raising his head slightly. 'Hector, you should not boast,' he said with difficulty, 'when you know that you have overcome me only with the help of the gods. If it had not been for Apollo, your spear would not be giving me unbearable pain. I have dealt with many men in honest fights and I might have withstood many more if Phoebus Apollo had not appeared. Only when I was defenceless, did Euphorbus dare to attack me – even then it was not face to face but with a cowardly stab in the back. You were only the third. I shall not live long; my limbs are getting weak and losing their strength and I can hardly speak, but remember what I have to say in my last moment: you haven't long to live either. You will soon die at the hands of the great Achilles.'

His head sank to his chest and a very quiet groan issued from his mouth. Hector leapt towards him, held his body under his foot and tore the blood-stained spear from the wound.

'Are you trying to frighten me with a prophecy of death?' he shouted defiantly. 'I am not afraid of your Achilles; just let him appear here. I will run him through before he knows where he is; the same as I have done to you, Patroclus, believe me.'

But Patroclus's ears were already deaf to any sound.

ACHILLES MOURNS PATROCLUS'S DEATH

Achilles was waiting impatiently for Patroclus to return. His friend had been away far too long and it was about time that he was back. Achilles found it hard to sit and do nothing. He could hear noise and shouts outside. What had happened? He feared the worst.

He was about to go to find out why there was such a lot of noise but at the door he ran into King Nestor's son. Antilochus was gasping for breath, his eyes were popping out and the corners of his mouth were drawn with pain. He could hardly speak:

'Achilles, King Menelaus has sent me with some terrible news. Your friend Patroclus has been killed. He was overpowered in a fight with Hector, stripped of the armour and his weapons too. Our men are now fighting for his dead body!'

Achilles staggered and nearly fainted. He caught Antilochus by the shoulders and shook him with horror: 'What are you saying

— Patroclus is dead? My best friend for years. Oh gods! How did it happen? Tell me all you know. Did he fight Hector alone? Did no one help him?'

'There were terrible things happening, Achilles, so horrible that I can hardly speak about them,' he stammered. 'It must have been Zeus's wish that Patroclus found himself against heavy odds. Hector gave him only the last blow. Then there was a dreadful fight around the dead body. They dragged him here and there. Your charioteer, Automedon, wanted to save your war chariot and to take it to safety, but when the horses saw that their master was dead, they roared up and wouldn't move.

'All at once the sky went black and then Ajax of Salamis prayed to Zeus. He said, "If we are to die, Zeus, at least give us a clear sky. Kill us in the daylight if you must, but as it is, we cannot even send a messenger to Achilles with the news!" I do not know if

Zeus was moved by this tearful protest, or what made him grant Ajax's request, but the sun shone on them and the fighting could go on relentlessly. Menelaus ordered all the soldiers to gather in a circle around Patroclus and protect his body. I was ordered to ask you for help. Oh, King Achilles, why did it have to be me who had to bring you the saddest news you could hear?' Antilochus broke down, sobbing and shaking.

When he raised his eyes, he saw Achilles sobbing quietly. Then Achilles sank to his knees and smeared himself with dust and earth. Then he threw himself down on the ground and beat it with his fists. He began to tear his hair out and scratch his face. Antilochus was worried that, in his despair, Achilles would cut his throat. He ran to his side and embraced him.

Achilles moaned and sobbed so loudly that even his mother, Thetis, heard him in her palace at the bottom of the sea. Thetis began to cry as she realized that her son's fate was sealed. She knew that she had to go to her

son and she asked her sisters, the Nereids, to go with her. 'Did any mother have to face a crueller fate? I bore Peleus a lovely, proud, lion-hearted son — he has always been my greatest joy. He had never caused me any sorrow, never hurt me until he decided to join the expedition against Troy. I did not hide from him what fate had in store, but for him, a soldier's honour has always been more important than danger to his own life. Oh my dear sisters, I know that I cannot save him, but I long to make it easier for him in some way.'

She and her Nereids soared from her cave under the sea to the surface. After a short journey, they stepped onto a rocky shore near to where the Greek fleet had dropped anchor in the first days of the war.

Thetis left her sisters and went up to Achilles who was falling deeper into despair, oblivious to the outside world.

'Achilles, what are all these tears for?' Thetis whispered. 'Even I can hear you in my underwater cave! Tell me your troubles and perhaps I can help you. You know I have pleaded with Zeus to punish the Greeks for the shameful way Agamemnon treated you.'

Achilles lifted his head and gently stroked his mother's arm: 'Is that you, mother? How lovely to see you, even on this sad occasion. Zeus, I know, has granted your wish and mine. The Greeks realize that they will not enter Troy without my help — but was it necessary for Patroclus to die? Patroclus! My dearest friend whom I loved as much as my own life. Hector killed him and stripped him of my weapons and my splendid armour. That was a dreadful thing to do. I must have my revenge, whatever the cost.'

'My unfortunate son, do you know what you are saying? You are signing your death warrant! It has been prophesied that if Hector falls fighting, you are doomed to die,' replied Thetis.

'I know, I know, mother,' Achilles admitted in a subdued tone. 'However, I should have been at Patroclus's side. I, the famed hero, winner of so many military expeditions, did not

manage to do for my friend what he would surely have done for me. No, no, no, my mind is made up: I will go now and destroy Hector. If I am doomed to die, then I hope I will be respected and admired. Mother, don't try to keep me from the field — that would get us nowhere. How I wish that gods and men would stop quarrelling and forget about wrongdoing.'

Once again he stroked his mother's arm and Thetis, whose face was wet with tears, cried in despair, 'But how can you fight Hector when you do not have your armour, your helmet or even your weapons? You cannot stand up to him with your bare hands. At least wait until I get you new armour. I will go straight to Hephaistos, the blacksmith of the gods. He owes me a favour. He will soon forge you new weapons. Promise me you will not do anything until then.'

'Alright, mother,' nodded Achilles with a deep sigh. 'I will put off my duel with Hector — but I must show myself to the Trojans. They are still fighting over Patroclus's body. If I appear on the walls, they will be terrified! Goodbye, mother. I know I am hurting you, but there is no other way open to me!'

They parted. Thetis set out for Olympus and Achilles, accompanied by Antilochus, hurried to the protective wall.

At the end of the plain, the Trojans were flocking around a handful of Greeks who were covering the body of Patroclus with their shields. It was being carried by Menelaus and Meriones. Achilles was distraught at the sight before him. He climbed to the highest point of the wall and with his legs astride, roared like a lion preparing to leap at his prey. He did not know that Pallas Athene was standing at his side and she had spread a golden cloud like a halo around him. The Trojans realized that Achilles was already preparing to go into battle. Immediately, their attacks died down and Menelaus and Meriones were able to move behind the fortress wall with Patroclus's body.

They laid Patroclus on a stretcher in the middle of the camp and all his friends began to gather around his body. All were sobbing loudly and paying their respects to Achilles's friend.

Standing over Patroclus's deathbed, the Greeks were filled with an urgent desire for revenge. Again and again Achilles embraced his friend, accusing himself for his death: 'Patroclus, my dearest friend, how wrong I was when I promised your father Menoetius that you would soon come back from Troy with a nice prize. Zeus decided otherwise. The gods often interfere cruelly in human affairs. You died honourably; I have still got this to come. But I swear to you: before the flames consume your body, I will lay Hector's cut-off head next to it, together with the armour and weapons that he took away from you. Until then, Patroclus, you will be guarded day and night, and all the captured women will weep at your side and cry instead of us who will go to fight Hector. I want to make amends for my mistakes, Patroclus.'

Unable to sleep, Achilles cried over the remains of his dear friend throughout the night until day-break.

ACHILLES AND AGAMEMNON ARE RECONCILED

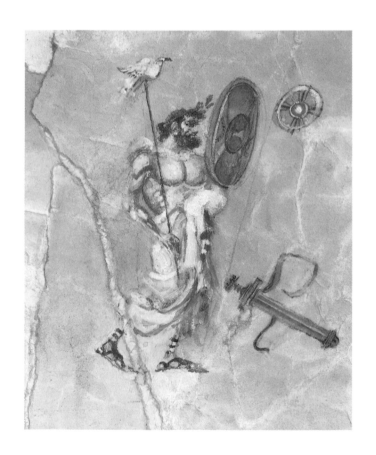

Thetis found her son before dawn, and gently took him by the hand. 'Do not grieve any more,' she said, 'it was Heaven's will that Patroclus should be killed. But look what I have brought you. Hephaistos, the blacksmith, has made you new armour – I have come straight from his smithy.'

'Oh mother!' cried Achilles, staring at the magnificent armour, the glittering shin guards and the golden-crested helmet. Achilles studied the shield closely. It was even more beautiful than the one lost in that unfortunate encounter. In its centre, Hephaistos had engraved a circle that was the earth and above it, heaven, with two smaller circles, the sun and the moon, and minute stars – the constellations of the Pleiades, the Bear and the bright Orion. Around the edges of the shield were three bands which depicted life on earth in various forms. The first band showed two cities. In one of them, a wedding was taking place. The bride was being brought to her new home accompanied by a procession of dancers. Further off, a case of some sort was being heard in a court and the sentence was being passed. The other city was not living peacefully; it was at war. The inhabitants had

been threatened by soldiers to give themselves up or face ruin. On the city walls were women, children and groups of old people, waiting anxiously to see whether the defenders would succeed in chasing the soldiers away.

On another band, Hephaistos depicted country life: ploughmen tilling a field, reapers at work with sharp sickles, and sheaf-binders who followed them and tied up the straw into bundles. The next scene was a vineyard, laden with grapes. A group of young men and girls were walking down a path in the middle. They were dragging baskets filled to the brim with fruit.

In the third band, Hephaistos had hammered three scenes from the life of shepherds. Brown cows were worked in gold, white ones in tin, and both looked very lifelike. Four herdsmen were accompanied by nine dogs who were being attacked by a pair of savage lions. Further on was a calmer scene. Sheep were grazing in a peaceful valley between their pens and the shepherds' huts, while some young people were enjoying themselves. A few peasants were watching the scene and others were looking round at two jugglers about to perform their tricks. The band was completed by a view of

the many forms of water with fish, otters, beavers, lobsters and other kinds of water creatures, and with creeks, waterfalls and headlands all depicted very realistically.

Achilles was so pleased with the magnificent work of Hephaistos that he cried. It was splendid and so, too, was the armour, the shin guards and the silver-rimmed helmet with a crest made of very thin gold lines. It was certainly true that no one else had such magnificent armour.

'I will put on the armour now,' Achilles said and he could not wait to join the fight. 'Only a god could make such a magnificent armour. All I want now is to come to grips with Hector — but what about Patroclus's body? I cannot just leave it here at the mercy of flies and worms.'

'Don't worry about that,' replied Thetis. 'I have a magic ointment of ambrosia and red nectar. It will preserve Patroclus's body for up to a year. But I must go now. Keep well and settle your disagreement with Agamemnon in public so that everybody will see that you have no more quarrels.'

Achilles hugged his mother and went to the camp calling for the Greek leaders. The whole camp was in great excitement. Everyone, soldiers and civilians alike, came out to hear what Achilles had to say. The front seats in the Assembly were taken by the great heroes. Using his spear as a staff, the wounded Odysseus came limping in, Diomedes sat beside him, the two men called Ajax came rushing in, making loud noises with their swords, and Nestor, Menelaus and Idomeneus also appeared. Last of all came Agamemnon, the Commander-in-Chief, with his arm in a sling as the wound below his elbow still had not healed.

The session was opened by Achilles. 'Great King Agamemnon,' he said with respect, 'I have been through very hard times in the last few hours and I have thought a lot about what happened between us. I asked myself: Did we really have to keep up our feud for such a long time? Why didn't we realize in time that the only ones who profited by our quarrel were Hector and consequently Troy? How many great Greeks have been killed on account of that? We can no longer help them but we can prevent others from being killed because of our feud!

ACHILLES AND AGAMEMNON
ARE RECONCILED

Let us no longer be angry with each other and shake hands as a sign of reconciliation. Agamemnon, King of Men, I no longer hate you and I want to go out immediately to fight the Trojans!'

Cries of joy broke out when Achilles had finished speaking and it took a good while before the enthusiasm of the Greeks died down and Agamemnon could reply.

'Friends, heroes of Greece!' exclaimed Agamemnon at last, raising his hand to quieten the Assembly. 'On more than one occasion, the Council of War has accused me of discouraging Achilles from taking part in our struggle. I am guilty of it; I have certainly acted too rashly in many ways. However, the fact is that the gods take advantage of our weak points and the goddess of Fury or Fate, or whatever you wish to call her, lurks in hiding and often blinds us all. Even the great Zeus himself was sometimes blinded by her, let alone a weak mortal like myself. However, I too will shake hands. Achilles, all the gifts that Odysseus told you about before are still yours!'

'Thank you, your majesty,' Achilles replied. 'You have made a good choice. But now there is no question of gifts and presents. Hector is the only one that matters. We must push forward against the Trojans and let them see that Achilles, in his splendid new armour, is fighting side by side with Agamemnon in the front ranks!'

'Well said, Achilles,' Odysseus intervened, 'I agree with your decision, but you mustn't forget that not all the soldiers are as fresh as your Myrmidons. It is not good to fight on an empty stomach; a soldier needs to be rested and nourished. I suggest that Agamemnon gives a rich banquet in your honour and as a token of reconciliation. Let him present his gifts to you before it starts. It will also raise the fighting spirit of the armies.'

'All right, Odysseus. I agree,' replied Agamemnon and clapped his hands several times. 'Let the youngest soldiers start bringing the gifts for the King of the Myrmidons. And bring Briseïs as well — I give her back to you, Achilles, just as I had taken her away from you. Prepare everything for a banquet. Before the fight begins I want to make a sacrifice to Zeus!'

The whole camp was filled with enthusiasm. Warriors hugged one another, cried out with joy, and beat the flat blades of their swords against their shields and threw their bows and spears up into the air.

A pig was brought to Agamemnon who cut off a tuft of its bristles and threw it into the fire in honour of Zeus. Then he asked for forgiveness for everything that he had ever done to offend Achilles. When he had finished, Achilles did the same.

Everybody listened to them with respect and when the pig had been cooked they offered each other the best pieces and told each other wartime stories. But Achilles seemed to be rather depressed. He ate only a few mouthfuls, stood for a while beside Patroclus and went off to his tent. He was still feeling guilty for his friend's death and there was no shaking it off.

The noise and shouting from outside roused him from his gloom and reminded him it was time to get ready for the fight. He tested his new armour: his breastplate fitted him like a glove, the shin guards clung perfectly and the massive helmet with the golden crest sat firmly on his head. Achilles took his spear from its case, weighed it in his hand and called to Automedon to harness the horses.

When he heard the horses neighing, he went out, leapt into the chariot, picked up the shining whip with its golden handle and cracked it over the horses' heads. 'Hurry, Xanthus and Balius, we are going to fight Hector. And make sure you bring us home safely. Gallop as fast as you can so that I don't fall into the hands of the Trojans as Patroclus did!'

The horses neighed, shook their manes and Xanthus, to whom Hera had given human speech, tossed his head and spoke to Achilles: 'We can still bring you back safe today, but your fateful day is not far away. The gods decided on the death of Patroclus and they will also decide when you will die. We cannot run away from this even if we run faster than our own father Zephyrus, the god of winds!'

'Xanthus!' called Achilles. 'Why do you prophesy my destruction? I know my fate well enough. So why do you remind me of it? Hector must pay the price for killing Patroclus — what is the value of friendship if the man who killed your best friend is not punished? No, my dear horses, in spite of all the prophecies, be as quick as you can.' And Achilles's eyes flashed with hatred for Hector.

THE SLAUGHTER AT THE SCAMANDER

Driven by a terrible desire to have his revenge on Hector, Achilles set out with his Myrmidons to capture Hector and drag him dead or alive to Patroclus's side. However, they searched far and wide for him, but he was nowhere to be found. Only Aeneas rode out now and then to show how courageous he was and to prove that he was not frightened of Achilles. Apollo, who still supported Hector, had arranged this so that Hector and the main Trojan forces would be behind the city walls in safety while Aeneas pushed back Achilles. Naturally, Achilles was bent on destroying everybody who opposed him. He rode out against Aeneas and, protecting himself from the shots with his new five-layered shield, he brandished his spear over his head.

'What a remarkable sight, Aeneas! Why are you showing off in the front line?' he shouted, derisively. 'Perhaps the Trojans have promised you something if you do away with me! But I have already driven you back once. You know it is not easy to match your strength against a hero with divine blood in his veins!'

'Achilles, do not try to frighten me,' grinned Aeneas. 'I know that your mother is the goddess Thetis and you also know that my mother is the goddess Aphrodite and that my father is a distant relative of the gods. Let's not boast to each other like two stallholders in the market! I prefer to let our weapons speak for us.'

His right hand thrust a spear through the air. Achilles only just managed to stop it with his shield at the very last moment. Although the spear penetrated two layers of bronze, it was stopped by the middle layer which was made of gold. Achilles laughed, flung his spear at his opponent and seeing that he had missed him, jumped forward with his sword drawn. Aeneas bent down, perhaps to pick up a

rock, but to Achilles's amazement, he was suddenly veiled in a shroud of mist. When it dispersed, it was as if the Dardanian leader had disappeared into thin air. All that lay in front of Achilles was his own giant spear.

'What has happened?' he cried in amazement. 'The spear is here but the person I aimed for has vanished. Have the gods intervened because they do not want him to die? That's fine with me. Let us forget all about Aeneas and carry on looking for that confounded Hector.'

Achilles was not wrong in guessing that Aeneas's disappearance had been the work of the gods. It was Poseidon who first deflected the spear and then took Aeneas away from the fighting. Although Poseidon was not fond of the Trojans, he felt sorry for Aeneas as he knew that it was Apollo, rather than Hector, who had put him up to meeting Achilles to delay the clash with Achilles and his men.

But had Poseidon really intervened? Were the gods once again interfering in the fighting, helping some and setting traps for others? The lord of Olympus, Zeus, had changed his mind and said that he had no objection to the gods helping either side as the moment of decision for Troy was not far away. He said that not even he could interfere with the fate of Troy as the future of men, gods and cities was decided by the Fates. He was only the guardian of fate not its ruler. Immediately he said this, Hera, Athene, Poseidon, Hephaistos and Hermes had a discussion on how to help the Greeks, while Apollo, Ares, Artemis, Aphrodite, as well as the river-god Scamander talked about how to make it easier for the Trojans.

Meanwhile, Achilles pushed forward determined to fight his way with the Myrmidons close to the walls of Troy. He killed all who dared to bar his way. Polydor, Priam's youngest son, was killed by a thrust of his spear in the middle of his back, many had their chest pierced by his spear or their helmets hacked to the very skull. Others perished under the wheels of his chariot. He was in a terrible rage; not even the god of war could have been aroused to a greater frenzy.

The Trojan army was trying to find shelter by the banks of Scamander river, but nowhere was safe from the catapulters and bowmen of the Myrmidons who were swarming like hornets. The fleeing Trojans were repeatedly pelted by a cloud of arrows and stones and they felt devastated when they saw Achilles himself with his five-layered shield by the river.

In an overwhelming desire to escape from Achilles, the Trojans hurled themselves into the river, but Achilles jumped into the stream and started thrashing about him with his sword. Before long the river was red with blood and the dead bodies were piling up. It seemed that Achilles's desire for revenge would never be satisfied.

The bloody harvest had grown so much that Scamander appeared before Achilles,

disguised as an old Man. 'Achilles, come to your senses! Can't you see how many dead bodies are already floating in my river? The river bed is full, the water outlets are blocked and you just go on raging and killing more and more. Stop the outrage. I am appalled!'

'I will stop it, of course I will, Scamander,' answered Achilles, 'but only after I have driven the Trojans back and after I have prepared the same fate for Hector as he carried out on Patroclus!'

'Madman! Very well, but fight on the dry land and not in my pure water,' burst out Scamander. 'Even if Apollo, who has already helped the Trojans so much, allows you to wreak havoc, I myself will not!'

With this, Scamander caused the angry water to leap into waves. To begin with, the waves merely flowed one over the other, but then they started forming whirlpools, the bottom currents surged and foamed upwards. The swollen water was rising and soon reached up to Achilles's knees. It began to swirl around

him and pull him down. Achilles staggered in the water as it beat his legs and seeking support, he only just managed to grab hold of an elm tree on the steep bank. He pulled the branches of the tree, but Scamander weakened the roots and the tree uprooted itself and bridged the stream from side to side like a beaver's dam. The roaring river rushed at Achilles, driving forward the rocks off the bottom, making him so unsteady that he nearly fell over.

Achilles felt himself rocking and the armour on his chest was ringing with every step he made trying to escape. He staggered and trod on the dead bodies that kept butting into him from all sides. All this time the stream was growing stronger and roaring even more wildly because Simoeis, Scamander's brother and god of smaller streams and springs, had joined him to raise a great surge and rush against Achilles.

For the first time since he joined the fight, Achilles felt frightened. He lost hope and felt that he would never get out safe and sound from the surge of the water.

And who knows what would have happened if, at that moment, when the waves were already as high as a house, Hera had not come to his rescue with her divine help?

ANOTHER FEUD AT OLYMPUS

Zeus's wife had been following Achilles's struggle from the Olympian palace. When she saw the swollen water rushing at him, she was appalled and called on her son Hephaistos, 'Hephaistos, can you see what is happening down there outside Troy? Should we allow Achilles's victory to be taken away by some lower god only because he is the lord of rivers and streams? This is not the way to interpret Zeus's kind words. Achilles must be helped! As the god of fire, you are powerful enough to create heat that will dry up that awful surge of water. Meanwhile I will ask Zephyrus, the god of western winds, and his brother Note, the god of southern winds and whirlwinds, to start blowing for all they are worth. Don't stop heating the earth please before I give you a sign.'

Hephaistos disliked interfering in power struggles. What he enjoyed best was working in his smithy making weapons and metal jewellery. However, he did what his mother wanted.

In a very short time, everything began to change on the plain. An immense heat fell on it, as if a thousand furnaces were burning.

The water began to dry up and soon afterwards the trees and bushes started smouldering. Eels and other fish were tossing about on the dried-up ground, panting for a drop of water and tormented by the fiery breath of Hephaistos. He burned everything to ashes — plants, animals as well as the bodies of the dead men.

'Hera! Hephaistos! Show some kindness!' Scamander shouted to Mount Olympus, for his river was already burning and all the water that was left was bubbling like a boiling kettle. 'I know why you are angry, but I promise not to meddle in this matter again.'

'That's enough, Hephaistos, you can stop the heat,' Hera decided,

'This applies to Apollo as well,' Poseidon chipped in. 'He too supports no one more than his Trojans and he is astonished that I am bitter towards them. No wonder! I built walls around their city, a magnificent fortification, and when the question of payment came up, Laomedon, Priam's father, ignored it and nearly threatened me. And you, Apollo, are siding with him!'

Apollo just waved his hand. After all, Poseidon was his uncle and it wasn't polite to quarrel with him on account of mortals. He would certainly have let the matter rest had it not been for Artemis who caught hold of him by the end of his robe.

'Are you just going to drop the argument? What is your famous bow for? You once said, in front of Zeus himself, that you would have the courage to challenge Poseidon. Now you have that chance!' she said.

'Artemis!' Hera flared up like a forest fire. 'If there is anyone making trouble, it is you. You should be ashamed of yourself! Stick to your hunting adventures and do not annoy me!'

In her annoyance, she shook Artemis by the shoulders until her bow, which went everywhere with her,

satisfied with having averted the danger to Achilles.

The other supporters of the Greeks were smiling and Pallas Athene even clapped her hands joyfully. But the ever-frowning, insufferable Ares, a supporter of the Trojans, rounded upon her: 'Are you pleased? You ought to be ashamed of yourself for goading on one Olympian against the other. You had better watch out.'

Out of sheer rage, he flung his spear at Pallas Athene, but she swerved and as quick as lightning she bent down to pick up a rock which hit Ares across his back. 'If it had not been for you, Troy would have fallen long ago and we would have been rid of this silly war,' she exclaimed.

fell to the ground. Arrows fell out of their holder and Artemis burst into tears. She ran to complain to Zeus about Hera. She knelt at his throne, but because she was sobbing so much she couldn't speak.

'Never mind, daughter, do not cry, you know very well how Hera shouts when she doesn't have her own way,' said Zeus soothingly. He was reluctant to be drawn into the quarrel and in any case, he found their argument quite amusing. He smiled and ran his fingers through his wavy beard: 'Wait a while. We shall all have dinner together. When you both taste the nectar and ambrosia you will instantly forget the bickering between you. I presume you don't want your divine bliss spoiled by human affairs.'

Apollo was the only god who didn't appear in the banqueting hall on Olympus. He was afraid that Achilles with his Myrmidons might launch an attack on Troy as soon as possible and he had the idea of giving the Trojans some more time for withdrawing behind the city walls. He went down to the plain by the Scamander river and disguised himself as Agenor, Antenor's son. He appeared in front of Achilles, who immediately went to attack him, but the Trojan fled. He dodged here and there, stopping now and then and looking back in faked terror, changing his direction, until eventually he stopped.

'Achilles, did you think that you would demolish Troy today?' called out Apollo, showing his true self to Achilles. 'You fool! You still have a lot to do to achieve that. You shall not destroy the city walls here at the river bank!'

Achilles gave an almighty cry. He turned round and started running to the Scaean Gate. He realized that he had been tricked and that Hector was probably out of his reach, safe behind the city walls.

HECTOR'S FALL

Achilles was mistaken. Hector was standing in front of the Scaean Gate and his gloomy eyes followed his warriors, who were thirsty, covered in dust, spattered with blood and rushing helter-skelter into the city. Hector was looking out for the last stragglers to appear. Above, on the battlements, King Priam agitatedly walked to and fro, observing what was happening on the plain. Suddenly he gave a start, turned to his group of courtiers and Queen Hecabe and pointed out something on the plain. Hecabe cried out and Priam leaned down over the gallery.

'Hector,' he wailed, 'Achilles is rushing here! Close the gates quickly and come up to join me on the battlements! That madman is after your blood and you are now the Trojans' last support and my only consolation in my old age. You must save yourself.'

'Hector, please listen to your father,' said the Queen wringing her hands. 'You cannot expect any mercy from Achilles! He will kill you and throw your body to the dogs. You will not even have a grave for us to visit.'

Hector did not reply. He just stood there like a statue, staring with glazed eyes at the battlefield, and gripping his spear with his sweat-drenched palms. His head was filled with heavy thoughts: 'Oh, King Priam, my noble father, oh, dear Hecabe, my beloved mother! Darling Andromache and my dear little son Astyanax, I know how worried you all are about me. I know that Achilles is stronger than I am, and I know I cannot expect any forgiveness from him. However, if I retreat into the safety of our castle, what will my soldiers say? I will be ashamed of myself. Polydamas, my adviser, will say that I did not listen to his advice and that I drove the Trojans and the allies into a lost fight. And many will say, "Look at Hector; dozens of men have died through his fault and he, when his turn comes, goes and hides from the enemy!" There is just one thing I could do: put away my weapons, go and meet Achilles half way and offer him a peace treaty. I could promise him that Helen will be returned to Menelaus together with all the treasures she brought with her, and that the Greeks will receive some compensation. But no, I am stupid to think that he would accept anything of the kind. There is only one way left open to me — to meet him in battle.'

When Achilles approached, Hector was terrified by the look in Achilles's eyes. Achilles was roaring so loudly and brandishing his spear so wildly that Hector thought that the god of war had disguised himself as King of the Myrmidons.

Hector felt that he must get away from Achilles. He ran along the city walls and then he turned in the direction of the road leading to the Scamander river. Full of panic, he ran back again to the city walls and was hoping to run through the gate, but Achilles was in hot pursuit and crossed his path in time. Once again they raced under the walls, around the fig trees to the banks of the Scamander where many Greek soldiers appeared. Achilles gave them a sign to leave their bows and spears alone. He wanted to deal with Hector himself. He didn't want an accidental shot by an unknown soldier to deprive him of the final triumph. They raced round the walls three times and as they reached the springs of Scamander, Zeus, who together with the other gods was following the race for life from the palace on Olympus, looked at the scales of Fate. He lifted them and saw that the scale with Hector's destiny had sunk low.

'Pallas Athene, your opportunity has come. Do what you have been dying to do,' he said in a dignified manner and sighed, for he did feel rather sorry for Hector after all.

Pallas Athene went down to the plain and, disguised at Hector's brother, Deiphobus, stood at Hector's side.

'Deiphobus, have you come to help me?' shouted Hector and his tired eyes flickered with joy. 'I have always loved you because you are so brave and I can see that I was not wrong. If you help me, I will surely overcome Achilles!' He stopped and in a loud voice shouted at the ruler of the Myrmidons: 'Achilles, now the

fight will begin and we will see who is the strongest. The gods must witness our duel as well as the promise that I solemnly give you. If I win, I will not destroy your body but will keep only your magnificent armour. I will hand over your body untouched to your soldiers. Will you promise the same?'

'What do you think, you damned fellow?' Achilles roared, in a surly manner. 'Do you think you can bargain with me? When you have caused so much harm to my Greek comrades and killed my closest friend? I hate you so much!'

In a blind rage, Achilles flung his spear at his opponent, but it missed. Pallas Athene, this time in her invisible form, picked it up and returned it to Achilles. Hector's morale was lifted and he threw his spear at Achilles, but it didn't penetrate his shield. The spear slid down and flew out of the reach of both contestants.

'Deiphobus, where are you? Give me my spear!' called Hector in despair, looking round in vain for his brother who had vanished into thin air. Hector realized that

he had been used as amusement by one of the gods and that he was now left to his own resources. He quickly drew his sword, stooped and thrust into Achilles, but Achilles had anticipated the attack. Protecting himself with his shield, he was approaching Hector step by step, looking for the weakest place in his armour — he knew it so well, as he had worn it himself so many times before. Suddenly Hector exposed his side to him and Achilles charged. The heavy spear pierced his neck. Hector fell into the dust, with only the faintest sound coming from his mouth.

'Hector, at last you reap what you have sown!' said Achilles in triumph and bent down over his defeated enemy. 'As you stripped poor Patroclus of his armour, I bet you did not think that your end would come so quickly. You dared to attack him thinking that I would always stay by the ships, but I have come back to defend my friend's honour. Now, he will have a proper burial, while your dead body will be thrown to dogs!'

'Achilles, please do not do that,' groaned Hector in his weakening voice. 'Let my wife and my parents have my body so that they can cremate it. They will give you a rich reward for it, a large amount of gold!'

'Never, Hector, even if they should pay ten times your weight in gold. I hate you more than anyone because you have robbed me of my best friend. Priam and Hecabe and your wife Andromache will never cry over your grave.'

'Achilles, your heart is as hard as iron, but just wait — your turn will come. And soon. You will be brought down by Paris and Apollo, maybe at the Scaean Gate!'

Hector had no strength to say anything more.

Hector died. He had no sword, no shield, no spear and Achilles stripped him of his blood-stained armour. Groups of the Greeks, who until then had remained at a distance, rushed towards the fallen man, gathered round him and several of them buried their weapons in his body.

'Greek friends, the gods have let me avenge Patroclus. Now without Hector, Troy will surely fall into our hands!' Achilles exclaimed excitedly and rushed to his war chariot, dragging the dead Hector behind him. He fastened him by the ankles to his chariot with leather straps and took up the reins himself. The horses cantered, the chariot was enveloped in thick dusty clouds and Hector was dragged behind along the ground.

On the battlements, the members of the Trojan royal household were desperately trying to prevent Priam from throwing himself down over the walls. He wanted to beg Achilles to hand over his son's body to him. Hecabe was wailing, her cheeks covered with tears, and she was tearing her hair and groaning incessantly: 'Why should I live now that my son Hector has died?'

At that moment Andromache, came out of her room, where she had been weaving the material for a new purple robe for Hector. Realizing that it was time to prepare his bath to wash off the

dust on his return from the battle, she called for her ladies-in-waiting. Hearing agitated cries and the sounds of wailing, she came out onto the porch of the palace. Her maids stood motionless, their shoulders shaking with sobbing. Overcome by a horrible premonition, Andromache ran to the battlements. She elbowed her way through the royal party, ran past the crying Priam and Hecabe, and searched the plain outside the city walls.

There, Achilles was dragging her Hector behind his chariot! She tore off her silver coronet, the wedding present from Aphrodite, the goddess of love, and her long hair fell over her face like a mourning veil.

The world went as black as night for Andromache and she fainted.

When she came round, her maids as well as the ladies-in-waiting were bending over her, their eyes darkened by a deep sorrow.

'Hector, my beloved husband, what has happened to us?' she whispered in a broken voice. 'I am now left alone and our poor Astyanax is an orphan. You were called the shield of the city, its protector — but what kind of future is in store for us when the protector has left us forever? And I was making such a wonderful victor's robe for you! I can only burn it. Your gift to us will be everlasting glory and a terrible sadness in our hearts.'

THE FUNERAL OF PATROCLUS

In the Greek camp, hundreds of Greeks were running from the ships which had been pulled onto the beach; the report of Achilles's victory flew faster than his war chariot. Both horsemen and foot-soldiers surrounded the King of the Myrmidons on all sides. They cheered him and paid him tribute by raising their spears and swords in the air. They were so elated that they would have preferred to return at once to attack Troy. However, according to an ancient custom they first had to honour the dead Patroclus by crying and wailing and riding round him in a mourning procession with the dead body of the defeated Hector. The jubilation was replaced by loud crying and wailing and Achilles himself was moved to tears when he addressed the dead man:

'Patroclus, my dearest friend, you can be at peace although to our great regret you are already in Hades's underground kingdom. I have carried out my promise to you. You have been avenged, the slaughtered Hector is lying at your feet. You will, of course, have a proper funeral, while Hector's body will be thrown away and given to the dogs. And you, my friends, who are crowding around me, have a rest after this day of bloody fighting, gather around the fires and recollect my friend's great achievements. We must celebrate Patroclus's memory as well as the victory that will open the gates of Troy to us.'

The soldiers cheered again at Achilles's words. He left them to go and report to Agamemnon on the hard struggle finally to overcome Hector. Agamemnon welcomed him, offered him a bath and immediately invited him to dinner with all the Greek commanders.

'Many thanks, great King,' said Achilles, 'but it is not right for me to bath and wash off the dust of battle before my friend's funeral. Please order the soldiers to prepare enough wood by tomorrow — the funeral fire must be as great as his contribution to our cause. And I will dine with you for a short while, but I want to sit by the seashore and remember Patroclus. Although I have avenged my friend, I am still very distressed by his death.'

The best of the Greek leaders joined the banquet held in Agamemnon's tent. The talk centred on the great achievements of war, with everyone paying tribute to Achilles's courage. All of them thought of the day after tomorrow and the day after that when the Trojans, afflicted by Hector's death, were sure to put up less resistance. However, Achilles, who usually enjoyed hearing compliments, seemed to be only half listening. He left the table early and went off with a very sorrowful look on his face.

He found a quiet place, a sandy promontory protected on three sides by a small rock, and stretched himself to rest his tired limbs. The sea was lapping soothingly at his feet and being so tired, he soon shut his eyes. Before long, he fell asleep. Suddenly, he heard some steps behind him, as if someone were approaching from the mainland, and a familiar voice said, 'What are you doing here, Achilles? I thought you were preparing my funeral and I can see you sleeping here while I wander in front of the entrance to Hades's underworld kingdom. But I can't go in before I am buried. Please do not put off the ceremony too long. It would be very painful for me. Or have you forgotten me entirely?'

Patroclus was standing in front of him, young and strong as he used to be, and staring at him with a pleading look.

'Dear friend,' whispered Achilles, waking up, 'how could you think such a thing? We are such close friends that there is nothing I would not do for you!'

'We are closer than you think, Achilles! It will not be long before, you, too, will be going my way. Now that you are seeing me for the last time, listen to my last request. When I was alive, we meant more to each other than our own brothers and such closeness cannot be divided even by death. Will you please put my ashes in the golden double-handled vessel which your mother once gave you and ask that your ashes, too, be added to them when you die? Let our ashes rest together. Will you promise, dear friend?'

His eyes were full of tears and Achilles couldn't utter a word. Silently, he held out his arms to hug his faithful comrade, but Patroclus's shadow vanished like a wisp of smoke blown away by the breeze.

In the east, the sky reddened and a new day was dawning, the day of the funeral. The camp was waking slowly but some soldiers, led by Merion, were already coming down the slopes of Mount Ida, bringing the trunks of oak trees for the large funeral pyre. On the shore, where the ceremony was to be held, the soldiers gradually built a gigantic pyramid of wood, a hundred feet wide and a hundred feet long. Many of the Greeks gathered around it waiting for the Myrmidons and Achilles to bring Patroclus's body.

The procession was led by war

chariots draped in mourning, followed by a mass of infantry, the spearmen, bowmen and catapulters who had all cut off locks of their hair as a sign of mourning. In the middle, Patroclus's body was carried on a bier and at the end walked Achilles, supporting the head of his dead friend in his hands.

The procession stopped at the pyre. As everyone watched, Achilles cut off a lock of his hair and in the gloomy silence, put it into Patroclus's unmoving hands. At the sign of it, the whole gathering broke out into heart-rending cries. They all bent their heads and kneeling down, picked up pinches of dust and sprinkled it onto their scalps.

The bowmen formed a passage in front of the pyre, and Achilles climbed up. Together with Nestor, Menelaus, Agamemnon and Odysseus he laid Patroclus's dead body on the very top. All around him lay the things that the hero loved most while he lived — his sword and his spear, as well as the double-handled jugs filled with honey and oil. Also by his side were four of his favourite horses

who had been killed so that they could accompany him on his journey into the underworld, plus dogs who guarded him. Twelve warriors whom Achilles captured in the battle at the Scamander river were brought in. When they were killed their bodies would burn alongside Patroclus's. Then Achilles put oil around Patroclus's body from head to feet so that the smoky fire would burn the body as quickly as possible.

The moment of parting had come. At Achilles's request the leaders gathered at the pyre. They lifted their spears high in their right hands and in silence remembered the dead hero. Only Achilles said a few words:

'Patroclus, there will be no other fighter like you. Accept the good wishes of your comrades. Your name will be living on. You will be a model for warriors and minstrels will write songs about you even when the rest of us are dead. You have died a hero's death, but I have carried out my revenge the way I promised you. I surrender your body to the fire!'

In a silence that ached with sorrow and pain, Achilles threw

a flaming torch upon the pyre.
A smoky steam arose, but only
a few flames licked the oak logs
and a hissing sound instead of
crackling was heard. The flames
went out as soon as they rose.
Achilles realized that he would
have to ask the gods of the winds
to help and he grabbed the
golden cup full of wine and started
pouring it out in a rich stream. As
if he had been waiting for this
mark of respect, Zephyrus flew
furiously through all the steps of
the funeral pyre, and blew up
every little spark. The fire
recovered, the flames leapt up
and began to flare high. With a

great crackling they enveloped
Patroclus's body.

Throughout the night, Zephyrus
and Boreas were blowing and
keeping the fire alive with their
breath. And all through the night
Achilles stood in front of the
burning pyramid, pouring wine
from the golden cup, while tears of
misery poured down his cheeks.

When daybreak came, the gods
of the winds returned home and a
comforting silence fell on the
shore. What was there left to do?

The fire had to be put out with
wine and Patroclus's ashes had to
be carefully gathered and put with
his bones into the golden jar
which Thetis had given to Achilles.

Again and again, while Achilles
was carrying out Patroclus's last
wish, his mind was occupied by
the thought that it might not be
long before his own ashes and
bones would be put with the
remains of his dearest friend.

He asked his comrades to
build a dignified grave for
Patroclus. Then Achilles ordered
that the whole army should take
part in a competition of games
and sports in honour of his
friend.

ZEUS'S DECISION

Zeus held his usual festive banquet, but this time the pleasant atmosphere nourished by the taste of nectar was missing. Apollo, in particular, was frowning and whenever he looked down to the Greek camp he turned indignantly in his reclining chair or exchanged an exasperated look with his sister, Artemis. In the middle of the meal he suddenly pushed his cup away and burst out:

'Have any of you immortals noticed how Achilles has been behaving outside Troy? For twelve days now he has harnessed his horses, tied Hector's dead body to his chariot and dragged him continuously around Patroclus's tomb! I don't like this one little bit and I am not the only one. After all, Hector always respected us and brought us numerous sacrifices — so I believe he deserves a descent burial, if only for the sake of his family. I propose that we send someone, perhaps Hermes, to the Greeks to steal Hector's body.'

'Apollo, you are forgetting that Achilles has divine blood in his veins!' said Hera, raising herself

on her reclining chair and striking the silver dinner table with her fist. 'Hector was only a mere mortal. Would you eventually drag him up to Olympus? Didn't you play the lute at the wedding of Achilles's parents? Don't try to defend anyone belonging to the Trojan royal family!'

'Calm down, Hera, calm down,' interrupted Zeus. 'It always comes back to that unfortunate apple that Paris handed over to Aphrodite,' he thought to himself. 'Hera may never forgive the Trojans for that! Hermes won't steal the body,' he went on, 'but I will call Thetis and ask her to give Achilles a talking-to. I will send Iris, my messenger, to fetch her straightaway.'

At Zeus's command Iris raced from Olympus all the way down to Thetis's undersea palace. The nymph was surrounded by other nymphs who were all distraught about her son's fate, but she immediately obeyed Zeus's instruction. She was dressed in mourning clothes when she stood in front of Zeus. He gave her a kind smile and beckoned her towards him.

'You have always been dear to me, Thetis, and I know that you have suffered a great deal on Achilles's account. However, I must tell you that the way your son has behaved lately has outraged many Olympian gods. For twelve days, Achilles has been treating his opponent's corpse in an undignified manner. I know Hector killed his close friend, but Achilles's revenge has gone beyond a joke. Tell him from me that he should surrender Hector's bodily remains to his father. At the same time, I am sending Iris to Priam with the suggestion that he should offer Achilles rich gifts as compensation. Achilles will not be offended and it will placate the outraged gods as well.'

'What an excellent idea,' said Hera quickly, who at last agreed with her husband. At the same time, though, she saw in Apollo's face the question: 'Why doesn't Zeus let one of the gods steal Hector's body?'

Thetis covered her face with her black veil and whispered dutifully, 'I will do as you want, great ruler. I know that your orders must be obeyed.'

ZEUS'S DECISION

She hurried down to the earth and while she was giving Achilles Zeus's command, Iris, the gods' messenger, went to see Priam.

Priam was in despair when Iris arrived at the royal palace. He was crying loudly and covering his head with dust.

'Calm yourself, King Priam,' said Iris, touching his shoulder. 'I have no more bad news for you. On the contrary! Zeus wants your brave son to be buried decently just as you do. Tomorrow you must go and find Achilles in his tent — only you and one charioteer must go. You must load the chariot with presents to melt Achilles's heart and you will ask humbly for Hector's body to be returned to you. Nothing will happen to you on the way or in the Greek camp. Hermes will join you and oversee

your safety. Achilles will be expecting you. You will come back with Hector and give him a dignified burial. This is what Zeus has decided.'

'I will be able to bury him as he deserves!' exclaimed Priam and lifted his hands to Iris, but she had already left the room.

At that, Priam wiped away his tears and hit the table with his sceptre: 'Servants, maids and guards, come here quickly. I must prepare for a long journey. Listen to my orders!'

He pulled himself up to his full height and it seemed that the hope of winning his son's body from Achilles suddenly made him feel young again.

IN ACHILLES'S TENT

From early in the morning, Priam's palace was busy. The servants were running about and carrying presents according to the King's instructions, putting some in a chest and others straight into the chariot. Priam kept an eye on them, at the same time talking to the Queen and his sons, Helenus, Paris, Agathon and Deiphobus, answering a dozen questions and issuing twenty instructions, conducting himself like a real king again.

'I hope it will work out,' moaned Hecabe. 'What if the Greeks capture you or even kill you? Would it not be better to stay here and mourn Hector?'

'You sound like my sons. Instead of taking Hector's place, they say we should hide behind the walls and wait until the Greeks are tired of besieging the city. Hector was a man — they are cowards who are interested only in hunting or dancing. And if I am destined to die in spite of what I heard from Zeus's messenger, I should prefer to die near my Hector. Sons, bring me my horses and have them harnessed!'

At last Priam's sons did something worthwhile. Pammon and Agathon ran off to fetch the horses, while Polites and Paris were pushing a brand-new chariot with magnificent wheels. Hippotheus and Helenus were preparing the harness. Priam excitedly mounted the chariot where his faithful charioteer, Idaius, was waiting. Suddenly Hecabe threw herself towards the King, crying, 'Offer a drink to the gods, Priam. Perhaps Zeus will send you a favourable sign to put all our minds at rest.'

Yes, a libation. The old King raised the golden cup handed to him by Hecabe, poured the potion out in drops and begged Zeus for his favour. Suddenly, an eagle with outspread wings appeared and glided above the castle. He approached the city from the right, which was a good omen for the journey.

'Let's go,' cried the old King, and the four-wheeled carriage moved forwards.

Priam's family accompanied them to the city gates and watched them as they drove across the plain until they were out of sight.

They stopped in the evening on the bank of the Scamander to let the horses refresh themselves. Suddenly a handsome young man approached them. He stopped in front of the King smiling, and spoke to him, 'How do you do? Where are you off to with such a load on your chariot? Are you not afraid of travelling on your own now that night is falling? Perhaps I could help you on your way, old man.

I expect you are heading for those ships which have been dragged up on the beach.'

Although the young man was smiling, Priam felt that it was still better to be safe than sorry: 'Who are you, young man? You are showing me great respect. And how do you know that we have a difficult journey? And why are you offering to help us?'

'Relax, Priam,' replied the young man, 'I am Hermes, and Zeus has asked me to take you safely to Achilles's tent. Give me your whip and reins. I will guide you through the Greek camp straight to him.'

He jumped up to the charioteer's seat, urged the horses on and before long they had reached the Greek's protective mound. They drove past the guards (Hermes used his magic wand which enabled him to send anyone he chose to sleep), and they arrived at the fence surrounding Achilles's tent. The only entry was through a gate secured with a heavy bar. Only Achilles knew how to move it; otherwise it took three sturdy men to open it. However,

Hermes managed to shift it easily and he led his charges to the commander's tent.

When Priam entered the tent, Achilles and his two friends, Alcimus and the charioteer Automedon, were sitting down to dinner. The Greek hero was just lifting his goblet of wine to his mouth, but his hand stopped in mid-air and his eyes almost popped out of his head. Was it really the old King Priam on his knees in front of him, stammering and begging him to answer?

'Achilles, you great hero, please listen to an old man's humble prayer,' he said sadly. 'You know I was forced to mourn many of my sons when they fell bravely in battle. But the worst blow came at the end of my life, when you, Achilles, overpowered and killed my dearest Hector. Has there ever been a more wretched man than me? I have got to kneel in front of the person who destroyed my greatest support. Have pity on me and hand over his body to me so that I can give him a decent burial. Please accept the presents that I have brought with me. Remember how your own father has always cared for you. He, too, has a miserable old age ahead of him, but at least he knows that his son is alive and that is the happiness I shall never know again.'

Achilles rose from his seat and gently pushed away the man's hands which were clasping his knees. The memory of his own father brought tears to his eyes and for the first time, he felt sorry for Priam.

'Priam, you have certainly suffered many wrongs in your life, but you are not the only one. Zeus has two jars, one containing blessings, the other evils, and it depends on him what mixture he prepares for us from those two vessels! One day is joyful, another sorrowful, one day there is a rise, another time a fall, one day brings glory, another shame. This applies to everyone. Even my own father, Peleus, received rich gifts from Zeus, but he was blessed with only one son. When I die, he will be left alone and there will be no one to comfort him, unlike you who have so many children. Get up,

Priam, your tears will not bring Hector back to life.'

'No, Achilles, I will not get up until you promise that I can take my son's body back to Troy to give him a solemn funeral. Please do as I ask and accept my gifts.'

'Why are you talking about gifts?' said Achilles, offended. Lifting the old man by his elbows, he added, 'I know well the will of the gods. My mother has told me that Zeus wants me to give you Hector's body. I expect your journey here was Zeus's doing, otherwise you wouldn't have dared to come. All right. I will order the maids to anoint Hector and to dress him in a beautiful white mantel and tunic and to prepare a bed for you in my tent. You will be able to take Hector with you!'

They came out of the tent together. Priam showed Achilles his presents — wonderful robes, kettles, a tripod and other objects. Automedon was sent to slaughter a white sheep and to roast it on a spit so that they could eat before going to bed.

'Priam, help yourself to a big piece,' said Achilles when they sat down to supper, 'and refresh yourself with this wine. It's too long since you have had a decent meal. Here, have this tasty piece of meat.'

The King accepted and took other pieces of grilled meat, too. As he did so, he looked at the graceful figure of Achilles and the thought crossed his mind that he almost had the beauty of a god. At the same time, Achilles looked at the old man and his wrinkled face, showing signs of suffering, made Achilles feel some respect for him. For a moment, they were bound together in mutual admiration.

Towards the end of the supper, when the slaves came in to take Priam to his room, Achilles shook Priam's hand.

'I wish you a good night, King. I expect you haven't had much sleep lately, so have a good rest tonight. But tell me: how many days are you going to devote to Hector's funeral?'

'As many as our tradition demands, Achilles. We shall mourn him in our homes and on the tenth day, the funeral fire will

be lit and its flames will burn Hector's body.'

'Well, King, let us observe a truce between us for those ten days,' said Achilles and bowed, crossing his arms on his chest. 'I promise you that for that length of time none of the Greeks will raise either his sword or spear.'

Then he took the old man's right hand again and pressed it hard. He had no idea that it was the last time he would see the father of his dead opponent. When he got up in the morning and asked for Priam, the maids showed him the deserted room and the untouched bedclothes.

For that evening the watchful Hermes appeared before Priam and told him to leave the Greek camp before the new day broke.

'You must set out at once! Achilles has spared your life, but what would happen if Agamemnon or another Greek commander discovered you? They have had no instructions from Olympus,' he warned him.

In silence, hidden by the darkness of the night, they laid Hector's body on the carriage and Idaius held the reins. Hermes used his divine power to move the heavy bar in the gate and let them out, unobserved, to the open plain behind the Greeks' protective mound.

When they were safely by the ford on the Scamander river, Hermes left Priam and went back to Olympus, his golden sandals glittering in the dark, starless night.

FAREWELL
TO HECTOR

When they reached the city of Troy, dawn was breaking. The sentries at the gate were only half awake and hardly noticed the King. Their eyes shut again the moment the rumble of the chariot had died down, but soon they, like the whole city, were awakened by a terrible noise. It was Cassandra. She had seen her brother wrapped in the white shroud on the royal chariot in the castle courtyard. She uttered a piercing cry as if a knife had stabbed her chest. Like someone demented, she began running around the courtyard, then she burst into the palace and cried so loudly that everyone in the city could hear:

'Hector has returned! He is back inside our city. Wake up and greet him like you did when he came home safe from a victorious battle!'

At once, the city roused itself from sleep and throngs of people began running towards the courtyard and swarming around the King's chariot. Loud wailing was heard everywhere, women put on veils, many of them fainting, while men bowed their heads. Hecabe and Andromache fell to their knees, tearing their hair, stroking the dead man's

face and cheeks and pressing kisses on his cold, unmoving lips. Priam had to force the crowd to make way for those who were to carry the hero's body to the palace.

Before midday, Hector's body was resting on a wooden bed in the royal throne room. At his head, his brothers and brothers-in-law stood silent and motionless, while at his feet a choir of royal singers sung hymns. Andromache's voice could be heard above the sound of the wailing:

'Hector, why did you die so young? Why did fate make me a widow so early and your son Astyanax an orphan? Why couldn't I give you some parting words which I would always remember? I know the Greeks will take revenge on us when

they conquer Troy; the gods seem to have given them permission. I will be unhappy for the rest of my life as I won't be able to save myself or Astyanax from being killed or from being sold as slaves.'

Next, Hecabe, choking with tears, also said goodbye to Hector: 'Hector, dearest of all my sons, my burden is heavier than the burden of Atlas who carries the world on his shoulders. You were said to be the darling of the gods and they must have loved you a lot for even after Achilles had dragged you so many times behind Patroclus's chariot, your body is still unmarked.'

Helen, supporting her mother-in-law, joined in with her warm voice trembling, 'My dear brother-in-law, I will never forget you. From the very first moment when Paris brought me to Troy, you were kindest of all to me. When I look back to the time when I came here, I wonder whether I ought to have come and been the cause of such misery — but I never heard a single harsh or spiteful word from you; you never held it against

me. How often you shouted down those who were unkind to me! The tears I am shedding now are also for my miserable self.'

For nine days, Trojan men and women throughout the city cried and moaned. From sunrise until night the crying and wailing resounded over the whole city until the tenth day dawned.

Priam ordered everybody to stop crying and to gather around the huge funeral fire that had been piled up over the past nine days. It was the largest funeral fire that the Trojans had ever seen. Afterwards, his brothers and his closest friends laid Hector's body on the very top and lit the fire.

The fire burned throughout the night. At dawn, Hector's brothers put out the flames with sparkling wine, picked up the bones and swept the ashes into a magnificent golden chest. They covered it with a beautiful purple cloth and laid it in a hollow grave, covering it with a mound of rectangular stones and closely-set boulders.

All the mourners then gathered in King Priam's palace, around

tables full of food and wine. They feasted for a long time and listened to a lute being played and songs being sung while they remembered the brave adventures of Prince Hector.

This was the traditional Trojan way of saying farewell to their heroes and Hector was certainly the most famous of them all.

THE FALL OF TROY

Hector was buried, the ceasefire ended and the fighting outside Troy flared up once again. Many of the Greeks believed that following Achilles's triumph, the Trojans would not be strong enough to resist. However, the city walls could still protect them well and they also received help from an unexpected quarter: hundreds of Amazons, warlike young women, led by Queen Penthesilea, arrived at the outskirts of the city. They came rushing in on horses, armed with swords, bows and spears, and launched themselves furiously at the Greeks.

Penthesilea even challenged Achilles to a duel. It was only after a brief struggle that Achilles succeeded in tearing the Queen off her horse and killing her with his spear. When he took off the Queen's armour and saw how beautiful she was even in death, he felt sorry for her. After the Amazons had agreed not to fight the Greeks any more, Achilles allowed them to take the body of their Queen away with them.

No sooner had the Amazons withdrawn than fighters from Ethiopia arrived. Their King Memnon was renowned for his good looks as well as for his undying courage, and in the battle that flared up as soon as his troops arrived, he proved his strength. He killed many Greek fighters, including Nestor's son, Antilochus, with his spear.

This was an event of special importance to Achilles. He had grown very close to Antilochus after Patroclus had been killed. He instantly set out to avenge his friend's death. In the fierce fighting, Memnon scratched Achilles's shoulder. The two men fought for a long time, until Memnon slipped and Achilles stabbed him with his spear. Shouts of triumph echoed across the plain and the Greeks prepared for a fierce assault against the city walls. Achilles fought his way through as far as the Scaean Gate and then, as he threw away his shield to break through the gate with his war axe, his fate was sealed. Paris, standing on the walls, released an arrow, led by Apollo himself, from his bow and instantly the arrow buried itself in Achilles's

heel, the only vulnerable place in his body which the waters of the river Styx had not touched.

Only a poet as great as Homer could have described that terrible moment. The greatest Greek hero sank to his knees with a cry, then got up using his last ounce of strength. He tore the treacherous arrow from his heel and flung it away. Blood flowed from Achilles's wound and he felt that his life was rapidly coming to an end. As he was dying, he let out a roar like a pride of lions. The ground shook and a crack appeared in the city wall. With his last words he cursed Troy, Priam's family and all the Trojan allies. The words of the prophet had come true: after the King of Aethiopia had died in a fight, Achilles died, too.

A terrible battle over Achilles's body broke out. The Trojans, jubilant that their greatest enemy had been killed, rushed to the plain, desperate to seize both Achilles's armour and his body. They wanted to drag it to the city and throw it to the dogs. However, led by Ajax and Odysseus, the Greeks managed to carry their dead hero to their camp.

For eighteen days, the Greeks mourned Achilles's death before they lit the funeral fire in the same place where Patroclus's funeral had been held. Hymns and funeral songs were sung continuously and the Greek commanders took turns to guard the funeral fire. People who came to honour his memory cut off pieces of their hair as a sign of mourning and, according to tradition, laid them by the dead body. Later on, after the fire had turned Achilles's body into ashes, they extinguished the embers with wine, put the ashes into the casket and mixed them with Patroclus's ashes, according to Achilles's wishes. Then a tomb was made from earth and stones over their casket. It was situated close to the shore to remind passing ships of the fame and glory of Greece's two greatest heroes.

And the fighting outside Troy went on ...

Soon after Achilles's funeral, Odysseus set out to look for Achilles's son, Neoptolemus, who

was living with his mother on the island of Scyros, and also Philoctetes, King of the Thracians, who was still leading a miserable life following his snake bite on the island of Chrysos. Agamemnon asked Odysseus to bring both of them to the Greek troops, for, according to the prophecy, Troy could never be taken without their help. Neoptolemus did not take long to be persuaded by Odysseus, for he longed to avenge his father's death. However, Philoctetes would not hear of fighting alongside Menelaus and Agamemnon. He regarded them as the chief cause of his miseries. But Odysseus tricked him into boarding Neoptolemus's ship under the pretext that he would be taken to his own country. Only on the journey did Odysseus tell him the truth, but he said that it was for his own good, as Philoctetes's wounds could only be cured outside Troy.

And he was right, after all. In his very first encounter, Philoctetes hit Paris with his poisoned arrow. Although he had been in solitude for such a long time, he had not lost his skill with his bow. And while Paris was dying in agony, Philoctetes's wounds healed as if by a miracle!

Although the Greeks were filled with courage and determination, their attacks continued to be thrown back by the strong Trojan walls. The walls seemed to be impregnable and defended the city well. However, walls are not always strong enough to avoid tricks, particularly one like Odysseus thought up.

'Let us build a large wooden horse,' he suggested, 'and hide our bravest fighters inside it. We will take it on the plain and most of us will pretend to leave and wait in hiding until the curious Trojans open the city gates and pour outside. Then our chance will come and we will attack them from two sides.'

When the prophet Calchas declared that Odysseus's plan would be successful, Agamemnon called for Epeius, the famous prize fighter and artist, and ordered him and his helpers to build a huge wooden

horse with a spacious empty stomach. With the help of Pallas Athene, Epeius finished his task in a short time. When the work was done, Menelaus, Odysseus, Diomedes, Philoctetes, Ajax, Neoptolemus and other fighters shut themselves inside the horse, while not far away, a man named Sinon was left behind chained up. Then the rest of the Greeks set fire to their camp, launched their ships and sailed away.

When morning came, the Trojans saw the smoking fires and the silhouettes of sails on the horizon. They poured out from the city, onto the plain and to the seashore. Everywhere it was empty and lifeless, only weapons lying here and there showed that it used to be a military camp. Firmly convinced that the war was over, the Trojans began to hug one another and dance for joy.

When they saw the gigantic wooden horse, they started looking round it and wondering where the odd monster had come from. Some admired it, others feared it, some suggested it should be thrown into the sea, while others said that it should be taken to the city where it could be examined properly.

Laocoon, a priest of Apollo, believed that it was some kind of trick — the Trojans ought to know better than anyone else how cunning their enemies could be. 'Beware of the Greeks even when they give you a present,' he warned them, but the Trojans did not take his words seriously. What was there to fear now that Agamemnon's armies had withdrawn? Laocoon started probing the wooden horse with his spear — something seemed to clatter inside. At that moment, the Trojans heard a cry as they discovered Sinon, who was groaning and moaning and begging the people to save him. The Greeks, he lied, had wanted to sacrifice him to the gods so that their fleet would have a favourable wind! When Priam heard this, he spared his life and asked why the Greeks had left behind the giant wooden horse. That, too, was a sacrifice to the goddess Athene, Sinon explained and its size would prevent the Trojans from moving it behind

the city walls. If that happened, it would become their protector and the Greeks would be ruined.

'You liar!' cried Laocoon as a warning when Sinon had finished speaking, but at the same time two sea serpents appeared and, before anyone knew what was happening, they strangled the priest and his two sons.

'Athene is furious! Laocoon offended her!' shouted the Trojans. 'Let us drag the horse behind the walls; that will seal our victory!'

A throng of Trojans crowded around the horse. With their combined strength, they pushed it from the plain towards the walls. At the walls another huge crowd started pulling down the gate and the adjoining part of the walls, as the horse was too huge to pass through. When they had pushed it as far as the sacred hill in front of the temple of Pallas Athene, there was a great celebration. The Trojans carried jugs of wine from their homes, cheering and hugging each other, rejoicing that they were alive to see the day of victory.

The celebration carried on well into the night, until at last they all fell into deep sleep. Even the sentries on the walls and the maids in the palace fell asleep. Only Cassandra was awake and she stood alone on the walls. With tears in her eyes, she contemplated the city whose downfall was beginning.

When night fell, Agamemnon's ships returned to the bay without anyone seeing them. The crews waited for the agreed signal. The cunning Sinon secretly crept to the wooden horse and knocked three times on its hollow stomach. Silently the Greek warriors jumped out: first came Achilles's son Neoptolemus, then Menelaus, closely followed by Odysseus, Epeius, Agamemnon, the younger Ajax, Diomedes, and lastly the surgeon Machaon. In silence, as they had previously agreed, they each took their places in front of the most important buildings and palaces. All at once, the Greeks burst inside and began to kill the sleeping and unsuspecting Trojans. A fire was the sign for Agamemnon's troops to break in

behind the walls and join those who had already started the slaughter.

The destruction of Troy was a terrible sight. The Greeks showed no mercy; houses were set on fire and no one could save themselves for there was nowhere to run. All but one man was killed — Aeneas managed to escape with his son Ascanius and with his old father, Anchises, on his back. Peace-loving Antenor was spared but Neoptolemus did not spare King Priam and killed him in a sacred place. The Trojan women were taken prisoner and even Andromache, Hecabe and Cassandra were among the Greeks' prizes. Menelaus came upon Helen with his sword in his hand ready to kill her, but her beauty overpowered him before he managed to use his weapon and she was saved.

The ships leaving Troy nearly sank under the weight of their prizes: gold, jewels, statues and vases, rare fabrics as well as pearls weighed them down. But those taking away the prizes did not fully realize what a long journey they had in front of them. Not all of them would see their homes again and hardly any of those who made it home would enjoy their prizes.

At that time, Troy, however, was a thing of the past. The ruined walls of the palaces, the charred beams towering against the sky like hollow teeth, burned-out areas strewn with broken spears, javelins and

overturned chariots were all that remained of the once-proud seat of King Priam.

What Zeus had promised his wife Hera had come true. Troy had been destroyed and Priam's family wiped out. The great war was over.

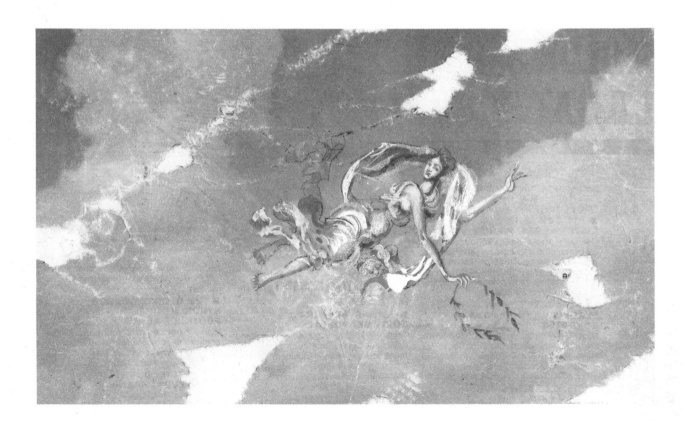